Two Grade Arithmetic

BOOK THREE

By K. LOVELL, B.Sc., M.A., Ph.D.(Lond.)

Professor of Educational Psychology, University of Leeds

and C. H. J. SMITH, B.Sc., M.A., Ph.D.(Lond.)

formerly Senior Lecturer in Education and Methodology of Mathematics, Borough Road College

GINN AND COMPANY LTD
LONDON AND AYLESBURY

Revised and reset 1969
First metric edition 1971
Revised metric edition 1975
Second impression 1976

Published by Ginn and Company Ltd.
Elsinore House, Buckingham Street, Aylesbury, Bucks HP20 2NQ

Product No. 112110533   ISBN 0 602 21884 5   (Pupils)

Product No. 112110622   ISBN 0 602 21888 8   (Teachers)

Printed in Great Britain at the University Press, Oxford
by Vivian Ridler, Printer to the University

PREFACE

I hope that these books will give you experience of working some important kinds of examples. Those on the right hand page are usually a little harder than those on the left.

Your teacher will tell you which examples you should work. If you try hard and work steadily and neatly, I hope you will get right all the exercises that you attempt, and that you come to enjoy mathematics.

Leeds
1971

K. LOVELL

ADDITION

First try these

1	35 +41	2	29 +54	3	62 +48	4	33 +57
5	113 +146	6	350 +219	7	426 +302	8	540 +146
9	215 +178	10	625 +137	11	473 +209	12	346 +238
13	347 +485	14	263 +179	15	455 +365	16	296 +604
17	106 97 +20	18	123 365 +82	19	248 557 +13	20	380 420 +107
21	1125 +2141	22	597 +3004	23	1129 +1590	24	2487 +2129
25	8475 +2968	26	7467 +6984	27	5821 +5376	28	6281 +9534
29	3761 2985 +4927	30	3950 7612 +2300	31	6351 5125 +4010	32	2976 3146 +8856

ADDITION

Now try these

1	46 +38	**2**	59 +37	**3**	68 +19	**4**	58 +61
5	315 +286	**6**	500 +428	**7**	198 +253	**8**	472 +385
9	172 5 +409	**10**	501 38 +206	**11**	613 291 +462	**12**	347 298 +515
13	4219 +1326	**14**	9071 +538	**15**	6291 +1582	**16**	5507 +1009
17	8976 +3202	**18**	6807 +4653	**19**	9903 +8841	**20**	5339 +4805
21	8123 7806 +3015	**22**	6102 4750 +9070	**23**	7159 9611 +6543	**24**	8952 6085 +6706
25	5438 8053 +107	**26**	1634 9909 +2803	**27**	5000 8123 +5996	**28**	9681 4803 +4005
29	8276 4135 +102	**30**	7951 1021 +8744	**31**	9827 8106 +7295	**32**	2198 8437 +9158

SUBTRACTION

First try these

1	58 – 40	**2**	67 – 25	**3**	96 – 32	**4**	48 – 11
5	74 – 54	**6**	92 – 39	**7**	60 – 23	**8**	47 – 28
9	55 – 16	**10**	31 – 25	**11**	598 – 427	**12**	328 – 105
13	671 – 240	**14**	887 – 423	**15**	438 – 216	**16**	361 – 145
17	408 – 239	**18**	627 – 440	**19**	752 – 367	**20**	930 – 182
21	4721 – 1309	**22**	3185 – 2713	**23**	5464 – 3452	**24**	7938 – 6067
25	8638 – 2559	**26**	6217 – 5368	**27**	4126 – 2786	**28**	9233 – 1679
29	13 298 – 12 174	**30**	22 765 – 11 962	**31**	31 765 – 15 310	**32**	38 420 – 13 407
33	24 982 – 17 056	**34**	37 219 – 28 976	**35**	34 287 – 19 518	**36**	46 002 – 27 311

SUBTRACTION

Now try these

1	81 − 25	**2**	64 − 47	**3**	90 − 53	**4**	76 − 39
5	238 − 162	**6**	820 − 278	**7**	735 − 418	**8**	643 − 389
9	2715 − 1328	**10**	9325 − 7130	**11**	2134 − 1956	**12**	8176 − 2057
13	5729 − 1439	**14**	9827 − 1956	**15**	4017 − 178	**16**	5512 − 1696
17	8431 − 2765	**18**	9003 − 4198	**19**	6418 − 1945	**20**	5303 − 1296
21	31 984 − 17 429	**22**	86 432 − 25 876	**23**	94 865 − 39 217	**24**	81 861 − 952
25	68 514 − 12 709	**26**	85 624 − 51 790	**27**	90 500 − 21 781	**28**	87 929 − 40 022
29	48 901 − 6 824	**30**	57 071 − 32 483	**31**	66 312 − 57 719	**32**	95 784 − 6 429
33	58 710 − 85	**34**	79 281 − 18 658	**35**	45 633 − 29 136	**36**	52 719 − 23 854

MULTIPLICATION AND DIVISION

First try these

Set 1

1	15 ×9	**2**	18 ×12	**3**	23 ×11	**4**	31 ×8
5	21 ×15	**6**	42 ×19	**7**	36 ×24	**8**	58 ×13
9	55 ×31	**10**	61 ×43	**11**	49 ×27	**12**	68 ×18
13	91 ×80	**14**	78 ×63	**15**	59 ×48	**16**	87 ×71
17	124 ×13	**18**	217 ×15	**19**	198 ×16	**20**	285 ×14

Set 2

1 $729 \div 9$ **2** $753 \div 8$ **3** $504 \div 12$ **4** $486 \div 11$

5 $232 \div 21$ **6** $525 \div 25$ **7** $610 \div 29$ **8** $390 \div 35$

9 $963 \div 31$ **10** $782 \div 37$ **11** $990 \div 45$ **12** $896 \div 28$

13 $988 \div 41$ **14** $881 \div 40$ **15** $441 \div 14$ **16** $688 \div 16$

17 $741 \div 17$ **18** $991 \div 18$ **19** $920 \div 15$ **20** $564 \div 13$

MULTIPLICATION AND DIVISION

Now try these

Set 1

1 $\begin{array}{r} 17 \\ \times 12 \\ \hline \end{array}$	**2** $\begin{array}{r} 24 \\ \times 9 \\ \hline \end{array}$	**3** $\begin{array}{r} 35 \\ \times 8 \\ \hline \end{array}$	**4** $\begin{array}{r} 57 \\ \times 6 \\ \hline \end{array}$
5 $\begin{array}{r} 25 \\ \times 16 \\ \hline \end{array}$	**6** $\begin{array}{r} 49 \\ \times 22 \\ \hline \end{array}$	**7** $\begin{array}{r} 74 \\ \times 28 \\ \hline \end{array}$	**8** $\begin{array}{r} 63 \\ \times 19 \\ \hline \end{array}$
9 $\begin{array}{r} 61 \\ \times 34 \\ \hline \end{array}$	**10** $\begin{array}{r} 72 \\ \times 49 \\ \hline \end{array}$	**11** $\begin{array}{r} 59 \\ \times 36 \\ \hline \end{array}$	**12** $\begin{array}{r} 83 \\ \times 28 \\ \hline \end{array}$
13 $\begin{array}{r} 96 \\ \times 81 \\ \hline \end{array}$	**14** $\begin{array}{r} 84 \\ \times 69 \\ \hline \end{array}$	**15** $\begin{array}{r} 67 \\ \times 57 \\ \hline \end{array}$	**16** $\begin{array}{r} 129 \\ \times 19 \\ \hline \end{array}$
17 $\begin{array}{r} 247 \\ \times 23 \\ \hline \end{array}$	**18** $\begin{array}{r} 316 \\ \times 28 \\ \hline \end{array}$	**19** $\begin{array}{r} 298 \\ \times 17 \\ \hline \end{array}$	**20** $\begin{array}{r} 265 \\ \times 31 \\ \hline \end{array}$

Set 2

1 $9\overline{)1827}$	**2** $7\overline{)2910}$	**3** $12\overline{)3768}$	**4** $11\overline{)6567}$
5 $22\overline{)2288}$	**6** $28\overline{)6468}$	**7** $37\overline{)7474}$	**8** $42\overline{)8620}$
9 $39\overline{)8610}$	**10** $46\overline{)9205}$	**11** $53\overline{)699}$	**12** $64\overline{)9600}$
13 $26\overline{)8086}$	**14** $15\overline{)9375}$	**15** $17\overline{)8874}$	**16** $21\overline{)9030}$
17 $23\overline{)9476}$	**18** $19\overline{)9899}$	**19** $14\overline{)9968}$	**20** $13\overline{)9791}$

PROBLEMS

First try these

1 Find the sum of two thousand, five hundred and one, and seventeen.

2 There were 3420 soldiers on a troopship. One-quarter got off at the first port of call. How many were left on board?

3 A bus has seats for 54 passengers. How many passengers can be carried by a fleet of 24 buses of this size?

4 The population of town A is 15 861 and that of town B is 9858   How many more people are there in town A than in town B?

5 Find the product of 195 and 17.

6 From twenty thousand take five thousand six hundred and three.

7 Find how many times 15 will divide into 975.

8 A bus carried 1052 people on Monday, 2105 on Tuesday and 1001 on Wednesday. How many passengers did it carry during these three days?

9 A merchant sold 156 boxes, each of which held one dozen eggs. How many eggs did he sell altogether?

10 From 10 000 take four times one hundred and twelve.

11 Find the sum of the numbers 2017, 2170 and 2710. Also, find the difference between the greatest and the least of these.

12 The smaller of two numbers is 782 and the difference between them is 156. What is the other number, and what is the sum of the two numbers?

13 Add 130 score to 42 dozen.

14 From the sum of 8257 and 4304, subtract 1926.

15 From 50 123 take 32 105.

16 How many hours are there in (a) 1 week, (b) 12 weeks?

17 Write in figures:
    (a) Nineteen thousand and six
    (b) Forty-three thousand five hundred and eleven
    (c) Thirty thousand and eighty-five

PROBLEMS

Now try these

1 How many strokes does a clock strike in 24 h, if it strikes hours only?

2 In an orchard there are 14 pear trees, twice as many apple trees, and seven times as many other trees as there are pear trees. How many trees are there in the orchard?

3 Take two gross from 7059.

4 There were 8579 visitors to a show on the first day, 5297 on the second and 7950 on the third. How many visitors were there altogether?

5 Find the product of 297 and 31.

6 The smaller of two numbers is 58, and their difference is 17. What is the larger number, and what is their product?

7 Divide the number which is 51 less than 1000 by 73.

8 When a certain number is divided by 40 the answer is 22. Find the number. Also, find the next highest number that is exactly divisible by 40.

9 Add 16 gross to 198 score.

10 Subtract 60 324 from 98 756. What must be added to the answer to make 40 000?

11 Find (a) the sum, (b) the difference, (c) the product and (d) the quotient of 336 and 16.

12 How often can 8 be subtracted from 34 296?

13 The number 25 600 is increased by one-quarter of itself. What does it become?

14 Write the largest whole number less than 70 000 which begins and ends with 7. How many times does the 7 of greater value contain the 7 of lesser value?

15 A newsagent sold a gross and a half of papers daily. How many did he sell in a month of 28 days?

16 Write in figures:
   (a) Ninety-eight thousand and five
   (b) Fifty thousand two hundred and seven

MONEY ADDITION AND SUBTRACTION

First try these

Set 1

1
$$£\\ 0{\cdot}29\\ +0{\cdot}18$$

2
$$£\\ 0{\cdot}36\\ +0{\cdot}14$$

3
$$£\\ 0{\cdot}07\tfrac{1}{2}\\ +0{\cdot}24\tfrac{1}{2}$$

4
$$£\\ 0{\cdot}65\\ +0{\cdot}13\tfrac{1}{2}$$

5
$$£\\ 4{\cdot}17\\ +2{\cdot}30\tfrac{1}{2}$$

6
$$£\\ 19{\cdot}63\\ +3{\cdot}45$$

7
$$£\\ 21{\cdot}59\\ 44{\cdot}81\\ +10{\cdot}02$$

8
$$£\\ 34{\cdot}52\\ 14{\cdot}39\\ +55{\cdot}47$$

9
$$£\\ 46{\cdot}77\\ 75{\cdot}32\\ +11{\cdot}04$$

Set 2

1
$$£\\ 0{\cdot}48\\ -0{\cdot}33\tfrac{1}{2}$$

2
$$£\\ 0{\cdot}67\\ -0{\cdot}59$$

3
$$£\\ 0{\cdot}91\tfrac{1}{2}\\ -0{\cdot}73\tfrac{1}{2}$$

4
$$£\\ 8{\cdot}64\\ -4{\cdot}51$$

5
$$£\\ 17{\cdot}25\\ -5{\cdot}54$$

6
$$£\\ 36{\cdot}61\\ -22{\cdot}98$$

7
$$£\\ 64{\cdot}25\\ -51{\cdot}36$$

8
$$£\\ 112{\cdot}30\\ -27{\cdot}74$$

9
$$£\\ 109{\cdot}41\\ -73{\cdot}96$$

10
$$£\\ 135{\cdot}51\\ -94{\cdot}79$$

11
$$£\\ 168{\cdot}81\\ -86{\cdot}92$$

12
$$£\\ 214{\cdot}52\\ -108{\cdot}74\tfrac{1}{2}$$

MONEY ADDITION AND SUBTRACTION

Now try these

Set 1

1
£
23·26
+68·14½

2
£
47·39
+59·28

3
£
60·18
+86·65

4
£
112·43
+77·69

5
£
214·85½
+322·76½

6
£
421·69
+18·02

7
£
66·43½
319·21
+126·67½

8
£
540·18
120·29
+65·53

9
£
51·91
97·16½
+439·78½

Set 2

1
£
0·64
−0·15

2
£
0·98
−0·59½

3
£
0·80
−0·16½

4
£
38·71
−2·48

5
£
53·37
−46·96

6
£
124·10
−0·17

7
£
481·02
−253·69

8
£
592·86
−368·90½

9
£
760·18
−97·08

10
£
872·57
−635·73½

11
£
649·62
−538·54

12
£
987·30
−829·25½

MONEY MULTIPLICATION AND DIVISION

First try these

Set 1

1 £ 0·21 ×5	**2** £ 0·13 ×7	**3** £ 0·17½ ×4
4 £ 1·34 ×3	**5** £ 2·87 ×5	**6** £ 1·69 ×7
7 £ 3·12 ×9	**8** £ 8·54 ×6	**9** £ 9·75 ×8
10 £ 11·36 ×4	**11** £ 21·98 ×7	**12** £ 10·71 ×10

Set 2

1 £ 6)0·72	**2** £ 7)0·91	**3** £ 10)0·60
4 £ 3)0·43½	**5** £ 4)16·28	**6** £ 5)25·05
7 £ 7)31·64	**8** £ 10)84·20	**9** £ 6)90·12
10 £ 8)145·84	**11** £ 12)90·78	**12** £ 11)132·60½

MONEY MULTIPLICATION AND DIVISION

Now try these

Set 1

1 £
2·68½
×9
_____

2 £
4·30
×7
_____

3 £
7·56
×11
_____

4 £
10·19½
×12
_____

5 £
14·86
×6
_____

6 £
32·37
×5
_____

7 £
41·72½
×10
_____

8 £
24·36
×8
_____

9 £
9·75
×11
_____

10 £
12·83
×12
_____

11 £
15·01
×7
_____

12 £
18·74
×9
_____

Set 2

1 £
6)15·78
_____

2 £
9)65·29½
_____

3 £
10)103·80
_____

4 £
12)89·64
_____

5 £
7)145·56½
_____

6 £
8)92·20
_____

7 £
7)69·73
_____

8 £
8)123·59
_____

9 £
6)181·64
_____

10 £
15)6·45
_____

11 £
17)36·04
_____

12 £
21)63·21
_____

MONEY PROBLEMS

First try these

1 Jack owes a friend £4·36. The friend owes him £3·85. How much money must Jack give his friend to be out of debt?

2 Fourteen similar articles cost £31·64. Find the cost of one of these articles.

3 What change will Mother have out of £10·00 after paying £6·60 for rent, £0·92 for electricity and £1·07 for gas?

4 How much money must I have to give £0·87½ to each of twelve children?

5 Find the sum of £5·50, £23·61 and £2·49.

6 A builder pays six workmen £8·75 each. How much money does he pay out altogether?

7 Share £93·50 equally among 11 people.

8 Take £7·82 from £66·14.

9 What is the sum of 2½p, 25p and £2·50?

10 A man is paid £8·16 per day. How much does he earn in a working week of 5 days?

11 How much must be added to £15·97 to make £27·54?

12 Find the value of one-quarter of £26·82.

13 Add together £52·68, £19·75 and £0·41, and subtract your result from £100·00.

14 Find the cost of 8 articles at £17·05 each.

15 A boy saved 15p a week for a whole year (52 weeks). He then bought a present costing £5·60. How much had he left out of his savings?

16 What is the total cost of 16 railway tickets at £0·44 each?

17 Add £120·00 to £50·00, and subtract £20·00 from your result.

18 Jack is an engineer and earns £43·35 per week. His sister is a typist and gets £27·25 per week. How much more money does Jack earn than his sister in 4 weeks?

19 How many articles, each costing 8p, can be bought for £4·96?

MONEY PROBLEMS

Now try these

1 Ten yards of material at £1·74 per yard are made into six curtains of equal length. What is the cost of each curtain?

2 A workman spends 18p per day on a return railway ticket and he travels to work 5 days each week. How much does he spend in fares in (*a*) 1 week, (*b*) 4 weeks, (*c*) 48 weeks?

3 A man has £297·45 in the bank. If he draws out £175·98, how much has he left?

4 Add together £40·30, £29·65 and £0·25, and subtract £50·40 from the result.

5 Divide £87·21 by 17.

6 To the sum of £9·17 and £5·03, add their difference.

7 £63·14 is divided equally among 4 men, 7 children and 3 women. How much does each get?

8 Multiply £16·05 by 17.

9 What sum of money added to itself is equal in amount to one half of £50·00.

10 Find twice the difference between £101·10 and £110·00.

11 A man earns 70p per hour. How many hours must he work to earn £18·20?

12 Find the cost of 20 chairs at £32·79 each.

13 A man paid £37·50 into the bank in January, £50·42 in February and £3·98 in March. How much money did he save in these 3 months?

14 A farmer sold 60 sheep at £15·00 each, and with the money he received for them he bought 15 cows. Find the cost of each cow.

15 How many articles each costing 13p can be bought for £35·49?

16 After paying one bill for £41·27 and another for £9·73, a man finds he has £20·61 left. How much money had he at first?

17 Share £110·40 equally among 24 people.

TRUE OR FALSE

All can try these

Write in your exercise book whether the following sentences are True (T) or False (F)

1     $8 + 2 < 1 + 5$

2     $13 - 5 > 6 \times 1$

3 The order in which we add numbers together does not matter.

4     $2 \times 9 = 27 - 9$

5     $4 \div 4 < 7 \div 7$

6     $0 \times 4 = 6 - 6$

7   $2 + 3 + 19 = 41 - 15$

8     $9 \times 8 > 8 \times 9$

9   $(2 \times 0) + 0 = 13 - 13$

10 The sum of two or more even numbers is sometimes an even number.

11   $(4 \times 2) + 6 = 26 \div 2$

12     $36 \div 6 < 72 \div 12$

13     $120 - 5 = 23 \times 5$

14     $24 \div 6 < 27 - 7$

15   $12 - 9 + 5 < 4 + 3$

16     $22 \div 11 < 4 \times 1$

17     $16 + 0 = (64 \div 4) + 0$

18     $15 - 10 > 2 \times 2 \times 2$

19     $13 + 7 > (4 \times 4) + 4$

20 The sum of an odd number and an even number is always an odd number.

21     $40 + 18 > 7 \times 6 \times 2$

22   $0 + 13 - 0 > (24 \times 0)$

MISSING NUMBERS

All can try these

Find the missing numbers which belong in the squared boxes to make the following into true sentences.

1 (a) $\square + 7 = 7$ (b) $9 \times \square = 9$
  (c) $0 + 6 = \square$ (d) $2 \times 1 = \square$
  (e) $13 + \square = 13$ (f) $\square \times 12 = 12$

2 (a) $8 + 4 = \square + 8$ (b) $5 \times 2 = 2 \times \square$
  (c) $\square + 6 = 6 + 10$ (d) $11 \times \square = 6 \times 11$
  (e) $15 + \square = 7 + 15$ (f) $\square \times 9 = 9 \times 5$

3 (a) $8 + 2 + 4 = \square + 8 + 4$
  (b) $\square + 9 + 5 = 1 + 5 + 9$
  (c) $4 + 3 + \square = 2 + 3 + 4$
  (d) $6 \times 8 \times 10 = 6 \times \square \times 8$
  (e) $9 \times \square \times 3 = 2 \times 3 \times 9$
  (f) $12 \times 11 \times \square = 16 \times 11 \times 12$

4 (a) $(4 \times 6) + (4 \times 3) = 4 \times \square$
  (b) $(2 \times \square) + (2 \times 2) = 2 \times 8$
  (c) $(\square \times 5) + (11 \times 2) = 7 \times 11$
  (d) $(3 \times 7) + (3 \times 6) = \square \times 13$
  (e) $(\square \times 4) + (\square \times 8) = 2 \times 12$

5 After you found the numbers what did the sentences tell you? First think about the sentences in question 1, then about those in question 2, those in question 3 and finally those in question 4.

WEIGHT ADDITION, SUBTRACTION, MULTIPLICATION AND DIVISION

First try these

Set 1

1 $7\frac{1}{2}$ kg + 12 kg
2 $10\frac{1}{4}$ kg + $11\frac{3}{4}$ kg
3 8 kg + 1500 g
4 750 g + 9 kg 250 g
5 4 kg 750 g + 2 kg 500 g
6 2 tonnes 300 kg + 5 tonnes 200 kg
7 3 kg 400 g + 6 kg 950 g
8 4 tonnes 100 kg + 3 tonnes 500 kg

Set 2

1 629 g – 489 g
2 2 kg – 320 g
3 4 kg 68 g – 50 g
4 12 kg 300 g – 8 kg 600 g
5 8 tonnes – 2500 kg
6 10 tonnes 400 kg – 3 tonnes 40 kg
7 13 kg 620 g – 9 kg 470 g
8 15 tonnes 8 kg – 12 tonnes 110 kg

Set 3   Multiply each of the following quantities by 2

1 7 kg 500 g
2 5 kg 750 g
3 12 kg 180 g
4 9 kg 680 g
5 10 tonnes 705 kg
6 13 kg 550 g
7 6 tonnes 360 g
8 11 tonnes 490 kg

Set 4   Divide each of the following quantities by 2

1 7 kg
2 6 kg 600 g
3 8 kg 700 g
4 11 kg 500 g
5 4 tonnes 200 kg
6 5 kg 160 g
7 13 kg 406 g
8 11 tonnes 50 kg

WEIGHT ADDITION, SUBTRACTION, MULTIPLICATION AND DIVISION

Now try these

Set 1

1 13 kg 740 g + 27 kg 675 g
2 14 tonnes 85 kg + 20 tonnes 483 kg
3 29 kg 253 g + 30 kg 835 g
4 56 kg 710 g + 64 kg 841 g
5 83 tonnes 49 kg + 30 400 kg
6 70 tonnes 196 kg + 36 tonnes 208 kg
7 107 kg 926 g + 84 kg 476 g
8 131 tonnes 450 kg + 97 tonnes 694 kg

Set 2

1 71 kg 500 g – 48 kg 730 g
2 94 tonnes 326 kg – 37 tonnes 831 kg
3 9 kg 329 g – 8726 g
4 68 tonnes 81 kg – 21 000 kg
5 84 tonnes 769 kg – 52 tonnes 967 kg
6 140 kg 863 g – 94 kg 275 kg
7 129 kg 205 g – 104 kg 492 g
8 181 tonnes 510 kg—76 tonnes 548 kg

Set 3   Multiply each of the following quantities by 2

1 10 kg 250 g	**2** 31 tonnes 600 kg
3 48 kg 700 g	**4** 28 kg 580 g
5 33 tonnes 830 kg	**6** 78 tonnes 939 kg
7 89 kg 621 g	**8** 57 kg 476 g

Set 4   Divide each of the following quantities by 2

1 23 tonnes 140 kg	**2** 109 kg 500 g
3 39 tonnes 580 kg	**4** 93 kg 428 g
5 77 kg 802 g	**6** 68 kg 604 g
7 116 tonnes 24 kg	**8** 80 tonnes 752 kg

WEIGHT PROBLEMS

First try these

1 An empty jug weighs 1 kg 100 g. Half full of water it weighs 1 kg 800 g. What will it weigh when full of water?

2 Find the total of $14\frac{1}{2}$ kg, 11 kg 700 g and $10\frac{1}{4}$ kg.

3 From 1000 kg take 589 kg.

4 If 3 bags of sand weigh 150 kg what will 12 similar bags weigh?

5 How many $\frac{1}{2}$ kg packets of tea can be made from 12 kg?

6 An empty lorry weighs 2010 kg. On it are placed 12 sacks of potatoes, each weighing 50 kg, and 2 bags of flour weighing 100 kg each. What is the total weight of the lorry and its load?

7 Multiply 18 kg by 3, and divide the result by 2.

8 How much wool is required to knit 1 dozen pullovers, if each requires 275 g of wool? (Answer in kg and g.)

9 A merchant had 70 tonnes of coal. He sold 5 trucks of coal, each holding 9000 kg. How much coal had he left? (Answer in tonnes.)

10 How many kilogrammes are the same in weight as 90 500 g.

11 A grocer made up 100 kg of sugar into 500 g packets. If 1 kg is wasted, how many packets are made up?

12 Three girls together weigh 84 kg. If one weighs 30 kg, find the weight of each of the others, if they are of exactly the same weight?

13 A lorry can carry 2000 kg. How many lorry loads will it take to move 50 000 kg?

14 A boiler uses 26 000 kg of coke in 13 weeks. If it burns the coke at a steady rate, how much does it burn per week? (Answer in tonnes.)

15 It took 6 h to carry away 20 520 kg of soil. What weight of soil was moved each hour?

16 A grocer bought 25 kg of coffee. Half of it he made up into 500 g packets and the remainder into 250 g packets. How many packets did he make altogether?

WEIGHT PROBLEMS

Now try these

1 A motor-car weighs 900 kg, the driver 80½ kg and a passenger 69 kg. Find the total weight.

2 A box weighs 20 kg. Find the total weight of a dozen such boxes.

3 How much wool is needed to knit 2 dozen pairs of socks, if each pair takes 105 g? (Answer in kg and g.)

4 From 682 kg take 463 kg, and add 27½ kg to your result.

5 Find the weight of a sack of flour, if 2 dozen sacks weigh 3000 kg.

6 Three crates weigh 80 kg, 65½ kg and 93 kg. Find their total weight.

7 A soldier weighs 75 kg and his pack weighs 24 kg. How much less than 100 kg is the weight of the soldier and his pack?

8 A lorry carries 200 cases of tinned fruit. If each case weighs 14 kg, what was their total weight in tonnes and kg?

9 A grocer had 12 chests of tea each holding 25 kg. He made up the tea into 250 g packets. How many packets did he make?

10 A van carries 750 kg of goods. What weight of goods will it carry altogether in making 15 journeys, if it has a full load each time? (Answer in tonnes and kg.)

11 How many 28 kg bags of beans can be made up from 2464 kg?

12 Find the total weight of 18 loaves, each weighing 1½ kg, and a dozen 1 kg bags of flour.

13 A coal merchant had 30 000 kg of coal in stock. He sold 6000 kg, 3500 kg, 750 kg, 10 000 kg and 250 kg. What weight of coal has he still in stock?

14 Find the cost of 20 kg of potatoes at 5p per kg.

15 A ml of water weighs 1 g. A 10 litre pail, half full of water, weighs 6½ kg. How much does the pail weigh?

TIME ADDITION AND SUBTRACTION

First try these

Set 1

	min	sec			min	sec			min	sec			h	min
1	3	24	**2**		2	35	**3**		4	47	**4**		6	13
	+5	16			+3	45			+6	29			+1	41

		h	min				h	min			days	h			days	h
5		9	44	**6**			10	55	**7**		15	2	**8**		26	3
		+3	19				+4	9			+1	14			+12	18

		days	h			weeks	days			weeks	days			weeks	days
9		35	13	**10**		8	3	**11**		2	0	**12**		5	4
		+4	16			+4	1			+6	5			+9	6

Set 2

	min	sec			min	sec			min	sec			min	sec
1	4	40	**2**		8	53	**3**		6	10	**4**		9	32
	−2	20			−5	29			−4	40			−3	51

		h	min				h	min				h	min				h	min
5		7	50	**6**			5	45	**7**			9	16	**8**			11	35
		−5	30				−4	18				−3	30				−7	48

	days	h		days	h		days	h		days	h
9	18	23	**10**	29	20	**11**	46	4	**12**	33	0
	−3	8		−15	10		−21	19		−12	14

	weeks	days		weeks	days		weeks	days		weeks	days
13	16	6	**14**	13	1	**15**	10	0	**16**	15	4
	−8	2		−3	6		−2	4		−9	5

TIME ADDITION AND SUBTRACTION

Now try these

Set 1

1	h	min	sec
	3	10	14
	4	7	28
+1	18	30	

2	h	min	sec
	5	29	18
	6	15	47
+7	20	13	

3	h	min	sec
	9	41	32
	1	39	25
	+54	51	

4	days	h	min
	3	15	40
	7	12	34
+9	8	57	

5	days	h	min
	6	18	38
	11	22	16
+10	14	12	

6	days	h	min
	8	17	20
		15	42
+16	1	56	

7	weeks	days	h
	10	6	20
	1	4	15
+11	1	17	

8	weeks	days	h
	14	3	19
	5	0	4
+19	3	6	

9	weeks	days	h
	16	2	12
	8	5	13
	+4	21	

Set 2

1	h	min	sec
	14	56	24
-5	19	48	

2	h	min	sec
	16	10	34
-11	23	58	

3	h	min	sec
	25	18	20
-21	37	35	

4	days	h	min
	18	20	7
-15	10	30	

5	days	h	min
	34	9	26
-21	18	48	

6	days	h	min
	42	11	37
-8	14	50	

7	weeks	days	h
	14	3	20
	-6	5	13

8	weeks	days	h
	26	5	7
	-9	6	18

9	weeks	days	h
	30	0	10
	-14	4	15

10	weeks	days	h
	28	1	6
	-9	0	21

11	weeks	days	h
	34	2	12
	-18	3	17

12	weeks	days	h
	41	4	18
	-20	5	8

TIME PROBLEMS

First try these

1 How many hours and minutes are there between
  (a) 06:30 and 10:15   (b) 14:20 and 18:45
  (c) 11:50 and 14:35   (d) 19:40 and 01:25

2 Write in figures
  (a) Half past two (morn- (b) Ten minutes past
     ing)   three (afternoon)
  (c) Twenty minutes to five (d) Quarter to eight
     (afternoon)   (morning)
  (e) Seven minutes to mid- (f) Quarter past one
     night   (afternoon)

3 A man is 30 yr old and his son is a quarter as old. How old is the son? (Answer in years and months.)

4 It takes my father 70 min to reach his office. At what time must he leave home to be there at 08:30, and how late will he be if he leaves home at 07:25?

5 I leave home at 08:27 and arrive at school, which is 1 km away, at 08:37. At what speed do I walk?

6 The light of a lighthouse flashes every 10 sec. How many times does it flash (a) every hour, and (b) from 20:00 to 06:00?

7 A train is due to arrive at a station at 11:53. Owing to fog it is 38 min late. At what time does it arrive?

8 Divide 12 h 6 min 32 sec by 2.

9 One clock is 8 min slow and another is 15 min fast. If the first clock shows the time as 02:50, what is the correct time? What time will the second clock show?

10 A child goes to sleep at 18:30 and sleeps soundly until 07:00. How many hours does he sleep (a) every night, and (b) in 1 week?

11 School begins at 08:50. If 2 h 50 min are spent on lessons, and break lasts 20 min, at what time does morning school end?

12 Buses leave a bus depot every 8 min from 06:30. At what time will the 16th bus leave?

TIME PROBLEMS

Now try these

1 How many hours and minutes are there between
   (a) 09:20 and 13:36   (b) 10:48 and 15:51
   (c) 11:45 and 08:22   (d) 21:14 and 05:23

2 Write in figures
   (a) Eight minutes to one (afternoon)
   (b) Seventeen minutes past three (afternoon)
   (c) Nineteen minutes to twelve (morning)
   (d) Twenty-seven minutes past seven (morning)
   (e) Five and twenty minutes to six (morning)
   (f) Nine fifty-four (afternoon)

3 A man starts work each day at 07:30 and works until 17:30. He has 1 h for lunch. How many hours does he work in a 5-day week?

4 A bus leaves town A at 07:45 and arrives at town B at 11:15. It leaves town B at 13:15 and arrives back at town A at 17:00. How long does it take on the journey from A to B and back?

5 A train travelling at a steady speed goes 5 km in 4 min. How far will it travel between 18:17 and 18:41?

6 How many seconds are there between 11:57 and 12:05?

7 One train leaves town X at 10:00 and reaches town Y at 18:25. Another leaves X at 10:05 and takes 1 h 18 min longer on the journey than the first train. At what time does the second train arrive at Y?

8 On a summer's day the sun rose at 04:10 and set at 20:16. How many hours and minutes was the sun above the horizon?

9 It costs 5p a minute to work a machine. How much does it cost to run the machine from 07:30 until 09:50?

10 A car is travelling at 90 km/h. Find (a) how many m it travels in 1 sec, and (b) how many m it travels in 5 min.

CAPACITY ADDITION, SUBTRACTION, MULTIPLICATION AND DIVISION

First try these

Set 1

1 2 litres 50 ml + 7 litres 480 ml
2 6½ litres + 5 litres 500 ml
3 10 litres 600 ml + 1 litre 700 ml
4 20 litres 300 ml + 3 litres 900 ml
5 19 litres 295 ml + 6 litres 820 ml
6 13 litres 460 ml + 2500 ml
7 12 litres 368 ml + 14 litres 603 ml
8 8 litres 109 ml + 11 litres 891 ml

Set 2

1 16 litres – 10 litres 500 ml
2 11 litres 250 ml – 7 litres 320 ml
3 23 litres 37 ml – 12 litres 40 ml
4 24 litres 190 ml – 6170 ml
5 17 litres 410 ml – 9 litres 260 ml
6 31 litres 648 ml – 15 litres 794 ml
7 40 litres 537 ml – 37 litres 828 ml
8 29 litres 900 ml – 22 litres 297 ml

Set 3   Multiply each of the following quantities by 2

1 6 litres 300 ml   **2** 8 litres 490 ml
3 9 litres 580 ml   **4** 2 litres 750 ml
5 15 litres 150 ml   **6** 3 litres 120 ml
7 11 litres 700 ml   **8** 19 litres 600 ml

Set 4   Divide each of the following quantities by 2

1 12 litres 200 ml   **2** 7 litres 56 ml
3 5 litres 240 ml   **4** 16 litres 800 ml
5 11 litres 160 ml   **6** 9 litres 320 ml
7 14 litres 980 ml   **8** 13 litres 72 ml

CAPACITY ADDITION, SUBTRACTION, MULTIPLICATION AND DIVISION

Now try these

Set 1
1 17 litres 285 ml + 16 litres 501 ml
2 12 litres 600 ml + 4200 ml
3 36 litres 430 ml + 28 litres 911 ml
4 43 litres 39 ml + 31 litres 654 ml
5 54 litres 859 ml + 41 litres 317 ml
6 67 litres 507 ml + 25 litres 296 ml
7 89 litres 245 ml + 65 litres 820 ml
8 102 litres 613 ml + 53 litres 947 ml

Set 2
1 16 litres 250 ml – 9 litres 46 ml
2 35 litres – 29 300 ml
3 30 litres 742 ml – 23 litres 129 ml
4 63 litres 837 ml – 59 litres 532 ml
5 73 litres 409 ml – 51 litres 956 ml
6 49 litres 201 ml – 26 litres 841 ml
7 100 litres 814 ml – 82 litres 607 ml
8 84 litres 619 ml – 41 litres 174 ml

Set 3   Multiply each of the following quantities by 2
1 17 litres 123 ml   2 38 litres 421 ml
3 23 litres 746 ml   4 50 litres 634 ml
5 68 litres 509 ml   6 96 litres 849 ml
7 90 litres 427 ml   8 118 litres 713 ml

Set 4   Divide each of the following quantities by 2
1 26 litres 240 ml   2 38 litres 882 ml
3 19 litres 396 ml   4 47 litres 798 ml
5 74 litres 464 ml   6 55 litres 642 ml
7 81 litres 970 ml   8 93 litres 48 ml

CAPACITY PROBLEMS

First try these

1 How many litres of milk are required to give 120 children $\frac{1}{2}$ litre each?

2 Water is escaping at the rate of $\frac{1}{2}$ litre every 5 min. How much escapes in $\frac{1}{2}$ h?

3 From a 40 litre churn of milk, 30 bottles, each holding 600 ml, are filled. How many litres are left in the churn?

4 How many $\frac{1}{2}$ litre bottles can be filled from two 50 litre casks after allowing 1 litre as wasted.

5 A family drank $1\frac{1}{2}$ litres of milk in the morning, 1 litre at midday and $1\frac{1}{2}$ litres in the evening. How many litres did they drink altogether in a week?

6 A tank holds 150 litres. How many times can a small bucket holding 6 litres be filled from it?

7 From 1000 litres were sold 280 litres, 56 litres, 90 litres, 85 litres. How much less than 500 litres was the amount left?

8 A car on a country journey goes 56 km on 4 litres of petrol. If the petrol is used at a steady rate, how far does it travel on $\frac{1}{2}$ litre?

9 Water flows from a tap at the rate of 3 litres per min. How long will it take to fill a tank holding 210 litres?

10 Out of 80 litres of milk a milkman sold 72 000 ml. How many litres remained?

11 Find the sum of 4 litres, 60 half-litres and $164\frac{1}{2}$ litres.

12 If 40 litres of milk cost £4·80, what is the cost of 1 litre?

13 If a lorry travels 20 km on 4 litres of diesel oil, how many litres are required for a journey of 90 km?

14 A liquid costs £3·84 for 4 litres. What is the price of $\frac{1}{2}$ litre?

15 A bicycle fitted with a small motor can travel 300 km on 8 litres of petrol. How far can it go on 24 litres?

16 What is the difference between 17 litres and $15\frac{1}{2}$ litres? What would be the cost of the difference at 6p per half-litre?

CAPACITY PROBLEMS

Now try these

1 A tank holds 37 litres 500 ml of water. How much will 2 tanks of this size hold?

2 A dairyman has 200 litres of milk to sell at 10 p per litre. How much milk is left over when he has sold milk to the value of £15·00?

3 Each hour 4000 litres of water flow through a pipe. How much water would flow through two such pipes in 15 min?

4 A cask holds 25 litres of water. How many 500 ml jugs can be filled from it?

5 How many litres are required for 8 persons for 6 weeks if each is allowed a $\frac{1}{2}$ litre bottle twice a week?

6 A shop sold 720 litres of paraffin on Thursday, $326\frac{1}{2}$ litres on Friday and 483 litres on Saturday. How much paraffin was sold during these three days?

7 A motor-car uses 4 litres of lubricating oil in travelling 3480 km. How many km does it travel to 1 litre of oil?

8 Thirty-five litres of a certain fluid cost £14·00. Find the cost of (*a*) 1 litre, and (*b*) 250 ml.

9 A water tank will hold 400 litres, but it has in it only 322 litres. To fill it a can full of water must be poured in 6 times. How much does the can hold?

10 An oil-stove burns 600 ml of oil every 6 h. How long will a 30 litre drum of oil last? (Answer in h.)

11 Multiply $7\frac{1}{2}$ litres by 2, and add 20 litres to your answer.

12 A tank usually holds 800 litres of water, but because of a hole near the top it can only be three-quarters filled. Find how much water it can now hold.

13 During May a farmer sent 420 litres of milk, twice a day to 8 dairies. If the milk was shared equally among them, how much did each get per day?

14 If a bottle holds 600 ml of fluid, how much fluid will a dozen such bottles hold? (Answer in litres.)

WORDS USED WITH LINES AND SHAPES

All can try these

Write the missing words in your exercise book.

1 Two lines that meet at right angles are ———— lines.
2 The distance around a circle is a measure of its ————.
3 A rectangle having four equal sides is called a ————.
4 The sides of a right angle are ———— to each other.
5 A cell in a honeycomb is in the shape of a ————.
6 In a circle the ———— is twice as long as the ————.
7 The angle formed by the hands of a clock at 0300 h is called a ———— angle.
8 A shape which has eight sides of equal length is called a regular ————.
9 If two lines which cross each other are perpendicular to one another, four ———— ———— are formed.
10 Two lines that meet form a ————.
11 The headquarters of the U.S. Army in Washington is housed in a building of five equal sides. It is called the ———— Building.
12 The distance between two points on the page of a book is measured in ————, between two points on a school playing field in ————, and between two towns in ————.
13 Two angles of a triangle cannot together add up to ———— ————.
14 Two lines in the same surface that do not meet are ———— lines.
15 If a rectangle is rotated about a side it sweeps out or describes a ————.
16 Any four sided figure is called a ————, but the word ———— indicates a shape with any number of sides.

FINDING AREAS BY COUNTING UNITS

All can try these

1 (*a*) How many unit half squares are needed to cover square 1?

(*b*) How many unit squares are needed to cover rectangle 2?

(*c*) How many unit squares are needed to cover shape 3?

(*d*) How many unit half squares are needed to cover shape 3?

(*e*) What is the area of the rectangle $WXYZ$ measured in unit half squares.

☐ Unit square

◺ Unit half square

2 (*a*) How many unit triangles are needed to cover triangle 1?

(*b*) How many unit triangles are needed to cover hexagon 2?

◺ Unit triangle

(*c*) How many unit triangles are needed to cover parallelogram 3?

(*d*) Find the parallelogram within $ABCD$ which has the largest possible area. How many unit triangles are needed to cover it?

LENGTH ADDITION, SUBTRACTION, MULTIPLICATION AND DIVISION

First try these

Set 1

1 3 km 200 m + 1 km 700 m
2 5 km 600 m + 2 km 400 m
3 7 km 300 m + 3 km 750 m
4 9 km 990 m + 3 km 880 m
5 4 m 25 cm + 6 m 43 cm
6 8 m 93 cm + 11 m 50 cm
7 9 m 38 cm + 10 m 63 cm
8 12 m 41 cm + 10 m 8 cm

Set 2

1 4 km 120 m – 3000 m
2 6 km 740 m – 1 km 610 m
3 7 km 950 m – 2 km 360 m
4 5 km 50 m – 3 km 900 m
5 10 m 49 cm – 6 m 32 cm
6 8 m 60 cm – 400 cm
7 9 m 72 cm – 5 m 93 cm
8 12 m 36 cm – 2 m 85 cm

Set 3   Multiply each of the following quantities by 2

1 2 km 200 m	2 5 km 490 m
3 8 km 350 m	4 9 km 500 m
5 3 m 28 cm	6 7 m 60 cm
7 10 m 82 cm	8 11 m 45 cm

Set 4   Divide each of the following quantities by 2

1 6 km 80 m	2 9 km 20 m
3 12 km 600 m	4 15 km 140 m
5 8 m 50 cm	6 13 m 62 cm
7 17 m 10 cm	8 20 m 90 cm

LENGTH ADDITION, SUBTRACTION, MULTIPLICATION AND DIVISION

Now try these

Set 1
1 15 km 310 m + 2 km 160 m
2 26 km 620 m + 13 km 480 m
3 39 km 845 m + 21 km 340 m
4 50 km 740 m + 64 km 955 m
5 42 m 16 cm + 29 m 70 cm
6 62 m 49 cm + 38 m 51 cm
7 97 m 83 cm + 14 m 21 cm
8 84 m 32 cm + 76 m 98 cm

Set 2
1 43 km 915 m – 36 km 110 m
2 30 km 60 m – 12 km 970 m
3 77 km 150 m – 25 km 630 m
4 110 km 275 m – 48 km 520 m
5 28 m 67 cm – 20 m 54 cm
6 65 m 36 cm – 52 m 69 cm
7 105 m 45 cm – 86 m 99 cm
8 121 m 17 cm – 38 m 29 cm

Set 3   Multiply each of the following quantities by 2
1 17 km 298 m   2 53 km 510 m
3 65 km 760 m   4 98 km 680 m
5 50 m 29 cm   6 84 m 90 cm
7 72 m 44 cm   8 103 m 70 cm

Set 4   Divide each of the following quantities by 2
1 24 km 874 m   2 56 km 540 m
3 57 km 382 m   4 73 km 394 m
5 85 m 6 cm   6 67 m 68 cm
7 99 m 82 cm   8 78 m 56 cm

LENGTH PROBLEMS

First try these

1 Susan is 1 m tall. What is the height of her sister who is $5\frac{1}{2}$ cm taller?

2 Find the difference between 9 km 30 m and 6 km 800 m.

3 A man measured a fence 18 m long by placing a stick along it 12 times. How long was the stick?

4 The distance between two points on a road is 4 km 200 m. A boy cycles between these points 5 times. How far does he travel?

5 How many metres are there in a $\frac{1}{4}$ km? How many metres must be added to $\frac{1}{2}$ km to make 1 km?

6 A swimming pool is $8\frac{1}{2}$ m wide. How far does a girl swim if she crosses the pool 9 times?

7 Divide 45 km 800 m by 2.

8 From 42 km take 15 km 900 m.

9 A roll of wire is 16 m long. What length of wire is there in 8 rolls?

10 Find the sum of 5 km 700 m, 4 km 350 m and 1500 m.

11 What length in m and cm must be added to $15\frac{3}{4}$ m to make 22 m?

12 From a ball of string, 20 pieces, each $1\frac{1}{2}$ m long, are cut. If 30 m remain, how much string was there at first?

13 A man cycles 8 km 150 m from home. On the return journey he has a puncture after travelling 5 km 400 m. How far was he from home then?

14 Add $\frac{1}{4}$ km, $\frac{1}{2}$ km and 220 m. (Answer in m.)

15 A swimmer moves $2\frac{1}{2}$ m at each stroke. How far does he move in taking 22 strokes?

16 A man's pace is $\frac{3}{4}$ m. How many steps will he take in walking $\frac{3}{4}$ km?

17 A tree is 15 m long. How many logs, each 26 cm long, can be sawn off, and what length tree remains?

18 Divide 19 km 50 m by 2 and add 5 km to the result.

19 What length must be added to 5 cm to make $\frac{1}{2}$ m?

LENGTH PROBLEMS

Now try these

1 A boy walks round a garden which is 120 m long and 40 m wide. How much short of ½ km has he walked?

2 A road 35 km long is to be divided into 14 equal sections. How long will each section be?

3 Find in metres the total width required for 18 tennis courts, if a width of 15½ m is allowed for each court.

4 John lives 850 m north of the school and Anne lives 1280 m south of the school. How far away from one another do they live? How much nearer the school is John's house than Anne's?

5 A postman walks 6 km 750 m daily. How far short of 45 km does he walk in a working week of 5 days?

6 The distance around a running track is 400 m. How far does the runner travel in making 6 laps?

7 Add together ¾ of 24 km, ½ km, 1760 m and 110 m. (Answer in km and m.)

8 Find the total length, in m and cm, of 24 pieces of cloth each 105 cm long.

9 Four pins can be made from 5 cm of wire. How many pins can be made from 20 m of wire?

10 Along one side of a road there are 21 houses and a field. The houses are each 11 m wide and the field is 60 m wide. Find the length of the road in m.

11 Posts are placed along a road 2 m 50 cm apart. Find the distance between the 1st and the 21st post.

12 Take ¼ of 6 km from ¼ of 6400 m.

13 What must be added to twice 1250 m to equal 3 km?

14 Sixteen curb-stones are placed end to end. If each is 1 m 30 cm long, what is the length of the curb?

15 How many posts, each 1½ m long, can be cut from 6 thin tree trunks, each of which is 18 m long?

16 By how much is 4250 m less than ¾ of 6 km?

17 Add ¼ km to ½ of 500 m. (Answer in km.)

NUMBER PATTERNS

All can try these

1 Look at this number square of side 5.

×	1	2	3	4	5
1	1	2	3	4	5
2	2	4	6	8	10
3	3	6	9	12	15
4	4	8	12	16	20
5	5	10	15	20	25

  (*a*) Write down the numbers in it which differ by 4, also by 5.

  (*b*) Write down the odd numbers, also the even numbers.

  (*c*) Find all the squared numbers you can.

  (*d*) Find the numbers made up of factors.

2 (*a*) Write down an even number of even numbers and find their total.

  (*b*) Write down an odd number of even numbers and find their total.

  (*c*) What did you notice about the two totals?

  (*d*) Write down an even number of odd numbers and find their total.

  (*e*) Write down an odd number of odd numbers and find their total.

  (*f*) What did you notice about these two totals?

3 Use counters or pegs, or other suitable material to help you work these examples. Find the numbers which have to go in the square boxes.

  (*a*) $1^2 + (2 \times 1) + 1 = \square$

  (*b*) $2^2 + (2 \times 2) + 1 = \square$

  (*c*) $3^2 + (2 \times 3) + 1 = \square$

  (*d*) $4^2 + (2 \times 4) + 1 = \square$

  (*e*) $5^2 + (2 \times 5) + 1 = \square$

  (*f*) $6^2 + (2 \times 6) + 1 = \square$

  (*g*) What do you notice about the numbers you have found?

NUMBER PUZZLES

All can try these

1 Answer these questions using counters or pegs if you need them.

(a) Begin with 1 and add the next odd number. What is your answer?

(b) To the total in (a) add the next odd number. What is the total?

(c) To the total in (b) add the next odd number. What is the total?

(d) To the total in (c) add the next odd number. What is this total?

(e) What do you notice about the totals you have found?

2 Jack went to the river with two cans, one a 3 litre can and one a 5 litre can. How can he bring back exactly 4 litres of water?

3 Express 100, using only 4 figures, all of them 9.

4 Find out if it is true that the number 24 has more divisors than any number less than 24.

5 Find the numbers that go into the square boxes:
(a) $5 \times 12 \times 4 = 2 \times 10 \times \square$
(b) $(10 \times 4) + (\square \times 7) = 9 \times 6$

6 Find the missing numbers in each case:
(a) 0, 1, 3, 6, —, —
(b) 50, 49, 47, 44, —, —

7 Find the sum of:
(a) The first six numbers.
(b) The squares of the first six numbers.

MONEY AND LENGTH REDUCTION

All can try these

1 Express the following amounts of money as indicated
- (a) 68p as new halfpence
- (b) 53½p as new halfpence
- (c) 87p as new halfpence
- (d) 94½p as new halfpence
- (e) £4·35 as new pence
- (f) £9·63 as new pence
- (g) £10·04 as new pence
- (h) £11·84 as new pence
- (i) £7·10 as new pence
- (j) £8·05½ as new pence
- (k) 184 new halfpence as new pence
- (l) 106 new halfpence as new pence
- (m) 170 new pence as pounds
- (n) 293 new pence as pounds
- (o) 536 new pence as pounds
- (p) 801 new pence as pounds

2 Change the following units of length
- (a) 2½ m to cm
- (b) 3¼ m to cm
- (c) 6 m 87 cm to cm
- (d) 9 m 56 cm to cm
- (e) 13½ m to cm
- (f) 17¾ m to cm
- (g) 15 km to m
- (h) 21¼ km to m
- (i) 30 km 800 m to m
- (j) 42 km 320 m to m

3 Change the following units of length
- (a) 870 cm to m and cm
- (b) 563 cm to m and cm
- (c) 1763 m to km and m
- (d) 4982 m to km and m
- (e) 1086 cm to m and cm
- (f) 9153 m to km and m
- (g) 2100 cm to m
- (h) 3780 cm to m and cm
- (i) 18 000 m to km
- (j) 29 560 m to km and m

TIME, WEIGHT AND CAPACITY
REDUCTION

All can try these

1 Change the following units of time

   (*a*) 9 min 56 sec to sec   (*b*) 12 h 36 min to min

   (*c*) 24 h to min   (*d*) 14 days 8 h to h

   (*e*) 26 weeks 1 day to days   (*f*) 1 week 3 days 12 h to h

   (*g*) 895 sec to min and sec   (*h*) 706 min to h and min

   (*i*) 1009 min to h and min   (*j*) 131 h to days and h

   (*k*) 197 days to weeks and (*l*) 908 h to weeks, days
       days   and h

2 Change the following units of weight

   (*a*) 4 kg to g   (*b*) 7 kg 315 g to g

   (*c*) 5000 g to kg   (*d*) 2468 g to kg and g

   (*e*) $2\frac{3}{4}$ tonnes to kg   (*f*) 10 tonnes 550 kg to kg

   (*g*) 32 tonnes to kg   (*h*) 30 000 kg to tonnes

   (*i*) 10 050 kg to tonnes (*j*) 9203 kg to tonnes and
       and kg   kg

3 Change the following units of capacity

   (*a*) 129 litres to half-litres   (*b*) 510 half-litres to litres

   (*c*) 2000 half-litres to litres (*d*) 725 litres to half-litres

   (*e*) $1\frac{3}{4}$ litres to ml   (*f*) 6718 ml to litres and
                            ml

   (*g*) 250 half-litres to ml   (*h*) 6000 ml to half-litres

4 Express

   (*a*) 480 ml as cu. cm   (*b*) 6218 cu. cm as ml

   (*c*) $2\frac{1}{2}$ litres as cu. cm   (*d*) 9500 cu. cm as litres

DIVIDING QUANTITY BY QUANTITY

First try these

Give remainders where necessary

1 Find how many times
   (a) 4p is contained in 20p
   (b) $8\frac{1}{2}$p is contained in 60p
   (c) 13 g is contained in 52 g
   (d) $2\frac{1}{2}$ kg is contained in 50 kg
   (e) 15 cm is contained in 1 m 5 cm
   (f) 200 m is contained in 1 km
   (g) $7\frac{1}{2}$ litres is contained in 30 litres
   (h) 13p is contained in 52p
   (i) 20 g is contained in 1 kg
   (j) 9 km is contained in $85\frac{1}{2}$ km
   (k) $12\frac{1}{2}$ sec is contained in 1 min
   (l) 4 litres is contained in 38 litres
   (m) 50 ml is contained in $1\frac{1}{4}$ litre
   (n) 1 min 40 sec is contained in 6 min 40 sec

2 How many children can each receive 18p from £2·16?

3 How many bags, each containing $\frac{1}{2}$ kg of sweets, can be made up from 12 kg of sweets?

4 String is cut into lengths 75 cm long. How many lengths can be cut from a piece of string $1\frac{1}{2}$ m long?

5 Milk from a 3 litre can is poured into a number of jugs each holding 600 ml. If there is no waste of milk, how many jugs can be filled?

6 A school morning is 2 h 55 min long. How many lesson periods each 35 min long are there in this time?

DIVIDING QUANTITY BY QUANTITY

Now try these

Give remainders where necessary

1 Find how many times
 (a) 9p is contained in £0·81
 (b) 60p is contained in 210p
 (c) £1·44 is contained in £5·76
 (d) 13 kg is contained in 260 kg
 (e) 27 g is contained in 810 g
 (f) 80 m is contained in 6 km 400 m
 (g) 56 g is contained in 840 g
 (h) 32 cm is contained in 8 m
 (i) 72 m is contained in 36 km
 (j) 1 km 400 m is contained in 14 km
 (k) 22 kg is contained in 484 kg
 (l) 1 tonne 300 kg is contained in 39 tonnes
 (m) 40 ml is contained in ¾ litre
 (n) 32 litres is contained in 256 litres

2 An article costs £0·36. How many of these articles can be bought for £10·80?

3 A road 63 km long is to be divided into sections, each 2 km 100 m in length. How many sections will there be?

4 How many bags of sand, each containing 24 kg, can be made up from 1 tonne 8 kg?

5 A machine takes 2 min 8 sec to cut out a piece of metal. How many pieces of metal will it cut out in 8 h?

6 £4·35 is shared equally among a number of children so that each gets 29p. How many children are there?

SIDES AND ANGLES OF IMPORTANT SHAPES

All can try these

Draw the following shapes (a) parallelogram, (b) rectangle, (c) rhombus, (d) square

1 Are the opposite sides equal?
    (a)   (b)   (c)   (d)

2 Are the opposite sides parallel?
    (a)   (b)   (c)   (d)

3 Are the opposite angles equal?
    (a)   (b)   (c)   (d)

Now draw in their diagonals

4 Do the diagonals bisect each other?
    (a)   (b)   (c)   (d)

5 Are the diagonals at right angles to one another?
    (a)   (b)   (c)   (d)

6 Are all the sides equal?
    (a)   (b)   (c)   (d)

7 Is one angle a right angle?
    (a)   (b)   (c)   (d)

8 Are the diagonals equal?
    (a)   (b)   (c)   (d)

REFLECTION, ROTATION, TRANSLATION

All can try these

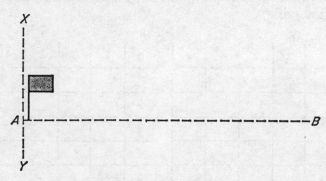

Show the position of the pattern after

(a) Translation along *AB*

(b) Reflection in *AB*

(c) Reflection in *XY* and translation along *AB*

(d) Rotation through 180° about *A*

(e) Translation along, and reflection in, *AB*

(f) Reflection in *XY* and rotation of 180° about *A*

(g) Reflection in *AB*, rotation through 180° about *A*, and reflection in *XY*

(h) Translation along *AB*, reflection in *XY* and reflection in *AB*

(i) How can we get the pattern in its final position in (h) back to its original position?

ADDITION AND MULTIPLICATION TABLES

All can try these

1 Complete (*a*) the addition table and (*b*) the multiplication table

(*a*)

+	1	2	3	4	5
1					
2					
3					
4					
5					

(*b*)

x	1	2	3	4	5
1					
2					
3					
4					
5					

2 Complete these addition tables

(*a*)

+	2	5
1		
4		

(*b*)

+	Even number	Odd number
Even number		
Odd number		

3 A boy faces South. Complete the following table showing if the boy is facing N (North) or S (South) after performing the actions indicated.

	Stand still	Turn through 180° clockwise	Turn through 360° clockwise
Stand still			
Turn through 180° clockwise			
Turn through 360° clockwise			

MODULO ARITHMETIC

All can try these

Complete the table for addition modulo (a) 3, (b) 4, (c) 5, (d) 6, (e) 8.

(a)

+	0	1	2
0			
1			
2			

(b)

+	0	1	2	3
0				
1				
2				
3				

(c)

+	0	1	2	3	4
0					
1					
2					
3					
4					

(d)

+	0	1	2	3	4	5
0						
1						
2						
3						
4						
5						

(e)

+	0	1	2	3	4	5	6	7
0								
1								
2								
3								
4								
5								
6								
7								

FINDING THE CROSS-SECTION
OF A SHAPE

All can try these

1

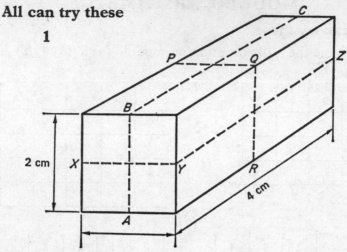

The rectangular block has a square cross-section of side 2 cm, and it is 4 cm long. Draw and describe the cross-section when it is cut along

(*a*) *ABC*   (*b*) *XYZ*   (*c*) *PQR*

2 *ABC* is a sphere of diameter 4 cm. *O* is the centre of the sphere. Draw and describe the cross-section when it is cut along

(*a*) a diameter *AOB*;

(*b*) a line *AC* which is not a diameter

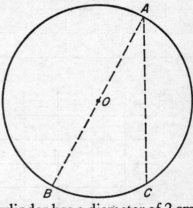

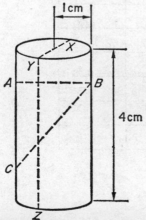

3 The cylinder has a diameter of 2 cm and a height of 4 cm. Draw and describe the cross-section when it is cut along

(*a*) a line *AB* parallel to the base

(*b*) a line *BC*

(*c*) a line *XYZ* where *XY* is a diameter and *Z* is vertically below *Y*

FINDING OUT

All can try these

1 When do $9 + 4 = 1$?

2 Find the missing number (a) $1 \div N = 4*$
         (b) $N \times 6 = 2*$
         (c) $N \div 4 = \frac{1}{2}*$

3 Is it reasonable to suggest that the classroom temperature should be 20°C? If not, what should the temperature be about?

4 Find the perimeter of a rectangle that is 20 m long and 8 m wide.

5 Give the correct name to each of the following angles:

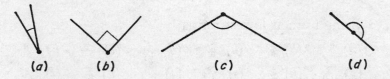

(a) (b)   (c)   (d)

6 In the number 33 what does, (a) the right hand figure tell you and (b) the left hand figure tell you?

7 In the number 404 what does the middle figure tell you?

8 Insert the correct signs in the following:
 (a) 100   1 = 100 (b) 374   0 = 0
 (c) 1268   1268 = 1 (d) 909   9 = 900
 (e) 625   25 = 25 (f) 100   100 = 10,000

9 The temperature in Alaska sometimes falls to 60°F below zero. How many degrees below freezing is this in °F? What is this in °C, to the nearest whole degree?

10 When do $2 + 2 = 0$?

EQUIVALENTS OF FRACTIONS

First try these

1 Find the missing numbers in the top line (numerator)

(a) $\frac{1}{3} = \frac{}{9}$ (b) $\frac{2}{3} = \frac{}{9}$ (c) $\frac{1}{4} = \frac{}{12}$ (d) $\frac{3}{4} = \frac{}{8}$

(e) $\frac{1}{2} = \frac{}{14}$ (f) $\frac{1}{5} = \frac{}{10}$ (g) $\frac{2}{5} = \frac{}{15}$ (h) $\frac{1}{6} = \frac{}{12}$

(i) $\frac{1}{8} = \frac{}{16}$ (j) $\frac{4}{5} = \frac{}{10}$ (k) $\frac{3}{4} = \frac{}{12}$ (l) $\frac{2}{3} = \frac{}{12}$

2 Find the missing numbers in the bottom line (denominator)

(a) $\frac{1}{2} = \frac{3}{}$ (b) $\frac{1}{4} = \frac{3}{}$ (c) $\frac{2}{3} = \frac{8}{}$ (d) $\frac{1}{5} = \frac{3}{}$

(e) $\frac{3}{10} = \frac{6}{}$ (f) $\frac{3}{4} = \frac{12}{}$ (g) $\frac{2}{5} = \frac{8}{}$ (h) $\frac{1}{6} = \frac{3}{}$

(i) $\frac{4}{5} = \frac{12}{}$ (j) $\frac{5}{6} = \frac{15}{}$ (k) $\frac{3}{8} = \frac{6}{}$ (l) $\frac{2}{3} = \frac{10}{}$

3 Bring to their lowest terms

(a) $\frac{2}{4}$ (b) $\frac{3}{9}$ (c) $\frac{2}{6}$ (d) $\frac{5}{10}$ (e) $\frac{7}{14}$ (f) $\frac{8}{16}$

(g) $\frac{2}{10}$ (h) $\frac{2}{8}$ (i) $\frac{3}{12}$ (j) $\frac{4}{16}$ (k) $\frac{4}{8}$ (l) $\frac{4}{12}$

(m) $\frac{5}{20}$ (n) $\frac{3}{15}$ (o) $\frac{7}{21}$ (p) $\frac{8}{24}$ (q) $\frac{6}{24}$ (r) $\frac{3}{18}$

4 Bring to their lowest terms

(a) $\frac{6}{8}$ (b) $\frac{9}{12}$ (c) $\frac{10}{15}$ (d) $\frac{12}{16}$ (e) $\frac{15}{20}$ (f) $\frac{16}{24}$

(g) $\frac{21}{28}$ (h) $\frac{18}{24}$ (i) $\frac{8}{24}$ (j) $\frac{10}{25}$ (k) $\frac{20}{30}$ (l) $\frac{15}{30}$

5 Which is the larger fraction?

(a) $\frac{1}{2}$ or $\frac{5}{8}$ (b) $\frac{1}{2}$ or $\frac{3}{10}$ (c) $\frac{1}{2}$ or $\frac{7}{12}$ (d) $\frac{1}{4}$ or $\frac{3}{8}$

(e) $\frac{1}{4}$ or $\frac{5}{12}$ (f) $\frac{1}{3}$ or $\frac{2}{9}$ (g) $\frac{1}{3}$ or $\frac{5}{12}$ (h) $\frac{1}{5}$ or $\frac{3}{10}$

(i) $\frac{3}{4}$ or $\frac{7}{8}$ (j) $\frac{2}{3}$ or $\frac{5}{9}$ (k) $\frac{4}{5}$ or $\frac{7}{10}$ (l) $\frac{2}{5}$ or $\frac{3}{10}$

(m) $\frac{5}{6}$ or $\frac{11}{12}$ (n) $\frac{2}{3}$ or $\frac{7}{12}$ (o) $\frac{3}{4}$ or $\frac{11}{12}$ (p) $\frac{2}{9}$ or $\frac{5}{18}$

EQUIVALENTS OF FRACTIONS

Now try these

1 Find the missing numbers in the top line (numerator)

(a) $\frac{1}{4}=\frac{}{16}$ (b) $\frac{1}{2}=\frac{}{10}$ (c) $\frac{2}{3}=\frac{}{18}$ (d) $\frac{3}{14}=\frac{}{28}$

(e) $\frac{4}{5}=\frac{}{20}$ (f) $\frac{3}{7}=\frac{}{21}$ (g) $\frac{5}{9}=\frac{}{27}$ (h) $\frac{7}{8}=\frac{}{32}$

(i) $\frac{2}{5}=\frac{}{35}$ (j) $\frac{7}{12}=\frac{}{36}$ (k) $\frac{8}{11}=\frac{}{22}$ (l) $\frac{1}{8}=\frac{}{40}$

2 Find the missing numbers in the bottom line (denominator)

(a) $\frac{1}{8}=\frac{3}{}$ (b) $\frac{5}{6}=\frac{10}{}$ (c) $\frac{3}{7}=\frac{9}{}$ (d) $\frac{2}{9}=\frac{8}{}$

(e) $\frac{1}{6}=\frac{5}{}$ (f) $\frac{3}{8}=\frac{12}{}$ (g) $\frac{7}{10}=\frac{28}{}$ (h) $\frac{1}{9}=\frac{3}{}$

(i) $\frac{4}{5}=\frac{16}{}$ (j) $\frac{11}{12}=\frac{33}{}$ (k) $\frac{5}{11}=\frac{20}{}$ (l) $\frac{3}{10}=\frac{21}{}$

3 Bring to their lowest terms

(a) $\frac{5}{20}$ (b) $\frac{6}{15}$ (c) $\frac{8}{24}$ (d) $\frac{9}{36}$ (e) $\frac{15}{30}$ (f) $\frac{12}{18}$

(g) $\frac{20}{32}$ (h) $\frac{16}{24}$ (i) $\frac{21}{28}$ (j) $\frac{24}{60}$ (k) $\frac{27}{45}$ (l) $\frac{22}{55}$

(m) $\frac{30}{45}$ (n) $\frac{25}{100}$ (o) $\frac{32}{96}$ (p) $\frac{28}{84}$ (q) $\frac{36}{84}$ (r) $\frac{28}{42}$

4 Using the numbers 2, 3, 4, 5, 6, 7, 8, 9, 10, 11, 12, make as many fractions as you can which are equal to

(a) $\frac{1}{2}$ (b) $\frac{1}{3}$ (c) $\frac{1}{4}$ (d) $\frac{1}{5}$ (e) $\frac{1}{6}$

5 Which is the larger fraction?

(a) $\frac{1}{2}$ or $\frac{1}{3}$ (b) $\frac{1}{4}$ or $\frac{1}{5}$ (c) $\frac{2}{3}$ or $\frac{3}{4}$ (d) $\frac{1}{2}$ or $\frac{2}{5}$

(e) $\frac{2}{3}$ or $\frac{3}{8}$ (f) $\frac{3}{4}$ or $\frac{4}{5}$ (g) $\frac{3}{4}$ or $\frac{5}{6}$ (h) $\frac{5}{8}$ or $\frac{7}{12}$

(i) $\frac{5}{6}$ or $\frac{7}{9}$ (j) $\frac{4}{9}$ or $\frac{5}{12}$ (k) $\frac{6}{7}$ or $\frac{11}{14}$ (l) $\frac{3}{5}$ or $\frac{4}{7}$

(m) $\frac{2}{3}$ or $\frac{7}{10}$ (n) $\frac{7}{12}$ or $\frac{3}{4}$ (o) $\frac{5}{8}$ or $\frac{2}{3}$ (p) $\frac{9}{10}$ or $\frac{7}{8}$

IMPROPER FRACTIONS, MIXED NUMBERS AND FRACTIONAL PARTS

First try these

1 Change to whole numbers or mixed numbers

(a) $\frac{6}{2}$ (b) $\frac{12}{3}$ (c) $\frac{3}{2}$ (d) $\frac{5}{4}$ (e) $\frac{8}{4}$ (f) $\frac{9}{4}$

(g) $\frac{11}{2}$ (h) $\frac{13}{5}$ (i) $\frac{16}{5}$ (j) $\frac{18}{6}$ (k) $\frac{19}{2}$ (l) $\frac{15}{3}$

(m) $\frac{14}{2}$ (n) $\frac{8}{3}$ (o) $\frac{7}{4}$ (p) $\frac{21}{4}$ (q) $\frac{17}{6}$ (r) $\frac{22}{5}$

(s) $\frac{29}{6}$ (t) $\frac{36}{6}$ (u) $\frac{40}{7}$ (v) $\frac{48}{8}$ (w) $\frac{44}{11}$ (x) $\frac{39}{5}$

2 Change to improper fractions

(a) $1\frac{1}{4}$ (b) $2\frac{1}{2}$ (c) $1\frac{1}{8}$ (d) $2\frac{1}{5}$ (e) $4\frac{1}{5}$ (f) $3\frac{3}{5}$

(g) $3\frac{3}{4}$ (h) $6\frac{2}{3}$ (i) $5\frac{3}{8}$ (j) $4\frac{4}{7}$ (k) $2\frac{1}{3}$ (l) $3\frac{1}{3}$

(m) $4\frac{3}{4}$ (n) $5\frac{1}{4}$ (o) $6\frac{1}{8}$ (p) $3\frac{3}{8}$ (q) $2\frac{1}{10}$ (r) $3\frac{4}{9}$

(s) $5\frac{7}{10}$ (t) $4\frac{7}{8}$ (u) $6\frac{2}{7}$ (v) $7\frac{5}{6}$ (w) $8\frac{1}{5}$ (x) $10\frac{1}{4}$

3 Find the value of

(a) $\frac{1}{2}, \frac{1}{4}, \frac{1}{8}$ of 1 m (Answers in cm)

(b) $\frac{1}{2}, \frac{1}{4}, \frac{1}{5}, \frac{1}{8}, \frac{1}{20}$ of £1·00

(c) $\frac{1}{2}, \frac{1}{4}, \frac{1}{8}$ of 1 km   (Answer in m)

(d) $\frac{1}{2}, \frac{1}{3}, \frac{1}{4}, \frac{1}{8}, \frac{1}{12}$ of 1 h   (Answers in min)

(e) $\frac{1}{2}, \frac{1}{4}, \frac{1}{8}, \frac{1}{16}, \frac{3}{4}$ of 1 kg   (Answers in g)

(f) $\frac{1}{2}, \frac{1}{4}, \frac{1}{8}$ of 1 litre   (Answers in ml)

(g) $\frac{1}{2}, \frac{1}{4}, \frac{1}{6}, \frac{1}{8}$ of 1 day   (Answers in h)

(h) $\frac{1}{2}, \frac{1}{4}, \frac{1}{8}$ of £4·00

(i) $\frac{1}{2}, \frac{1}{4}, \frac{1}{5}, \frac{3}{5}, \frac{1}{8}, \frac{5}{8},$ of £5·00

(j) $\frac{1}{2}, \frac{1}{4}, \frac{3}{4}, \frac{7}{8}, \frac{1}{16}$ of £40·00

IMPROPER FRACTIONS, MIXED NUMBERS AND FRACTIONAL PARTS

Now try these

1 Change to whole numbers or mixed numbers

(a) $\frac{15}{4}$ (b) $\frac{23}{4}$ (c) $\frac{29}{5}$ (d) $\frac{18}{5}$ (e) $\frac{25}{6}$ (f) $\frac{49}{8}$

(g) $\frac{40}{7}$ (h) $\frac{60}{11}$ (i) $\frac{53}{6}$ (j) $\frac{32}{8}$ (k) $\frac{60}{7}$ (l) $\frac{38}{9}$

(m) $\frac{56}{8}$ (n) $\frac{33}{10}$ (o) $\frac{82}{11}$ (p) $\frac{59}{12}$ (q) $\frac{93}{12}$ (r) $\frac{77}{9}$

(s) $\frac{64}{5}$ (t) $\frac{46}{3}$ (u) $\frac{85}{5}$ (v) $\frac{97}{8}$ (w) $\frac{84}{10}$ (x) $\frac{69}{9}$

2 Change to improper fractions

(a) $1\frac{5}{6}$ (b) $2\frac{3}{7}$ (c) $2\frac{1}{6}$ (d) $3\frac{7}{8}$ (e) $5\frac{9}{10}$ (f) $4\frac{6}{7}$

(g) $5\frac{4}{9}$ (h) $7\frac{2}{3}$ (i) $8\frac{3}{5}$ (j) $9\frac{1}{12}$ (k) $7\frac{5}{12}$ (l) $10\frac{3}{4}$

(m) $11\frac{2}{3}$ (n) $12\frac{5}{6}$ (o) $9\frac{7}{8}$ (p) $8\frac{2}{9}$ (q) $10\frac{5}{8}$ (r) $11\frac{1}{6}$

(s) $5\frac{5}{9}$ (t) $8\frac{6}{7}$ (u) $12\frac{7}{10}$ (v) $11\frac{4}{11}$ (w) $6\frac{3}{5}$ (x) $7\frac{1}{9}$

3 Find the value of

(a) $\frac{3}{8}, \frac{5}{8}, \frac{7}{8}$ of 1 kg   (Answers in g)

(b) $\frac{3}{4}, \frac{2}{5}, \frac{3}{5}, \frac{4}{5}, \frac{3}{8}, \frac{5}{8}, \frac{7}{8}$ of £1·00

(c) $\frac{3}{8}, \frac{5}{8}, \frac{7}{8}$ of 1 m   (Answers in cm)

(d) $\frac{3}{4}, \frac{5}{8}$ of 1 litre   (Answers in ml)

(e) $\frac{1}{2}, \frac{1}{4}, \frac{1}{8}$ of 1 min   (Answers in sec)

(f) $\frac{1}{2}, \frac{1}{4}, \frac{1}{8}, \frac{3}{4}$ of 500 g

(g) $\frac{1}{2}, \frac{1}{4}, \frac{1}{10}, \frac{3}{4}$ of 4 kg   (Answers in g)

(h) $\frac{1}{2}, \frac{1}{4}, \frac{3}{4}, \frac{1}{8}, \frac{1}{16}$ of 4 days   (Answers in h)

(i) $\frac{1}{2}, \frac{1}{5}, \frac{4}{5}, \frac{1}{10}, \frac{3}{10}, \frac{1}{20}$ of £100·00

(j) $\frac{1}{3}, \frac{1}{6}, \frac{1}{8}, \frac{1}{10}, \frac{1}{20}, \frac{7}{8}$ of 2400 m

FRACTIONS ADDITION (1)

First try these

Write the answers in their lowest terms

Set 1

1 $\frac{1}{4}+\frac{1}{4}$ 2 $\frac{1}{3}+\frac{1}{3}$ 3 $\frac{1}{5}+\frac{1}{5}$

4 $\frac{1}{6}+\frac{1}{6}$ 5 $\frac{2}{5}+\frac{1}{5}$ 6 $\frac{1}{5}+\frac{3}{5}$

7 $\frac{1}{7}+\frac{1}{7}$ 8 $\frac{1}{7}+\frac{3}{7}$ 9 $\frac{2}{7}+\frac{4}{7}$

10 $\frac{1}{7}+\frac{5}{7}$ 11 $\frac{1}{8}+\frac{1}{8}$ 12 $\frac{3}{8}+\frac{1}{8}$

13 $\frac{1}{9}+\frac{1}{9}$ 14 $\frac{2}{9}+\frac{4}{9}$ 15 $\frac{1}{9}+\frac{7}{9}$

16 $\frac{1}{10}+\frac{1}{10}$ 17 $\frac{3}{10}+\frac{3}{10}$ 18 $\frac{4}{10}+\frac{3}{10}$

Set 2

1 $\frac{1}{4}+\frac{1}{4}+\frac{1}{4}$ 2 $\frac{2}{5}+\frac{1}{5}+\frac{1}{5}$ 3 $\frac{1}{6}+\frac{1}{6}+\frac{1}{6}$

4 $\frac{2}{7}+\frac{1}{7}+\frac{3}{7}$ 5 $\frac{3}{8}+\frac{3}{8}+\frac{1}{8}$ 6 $\frac{2}{9}+\frac{5}{9}+\frac{1}{9}$

7 $\frac{3}{10}+\frac{1}{10}+\frac{3}{10}$ 8 $\frac{1}{7}+\frac{3}{7}+\frac{2}{7}$ 9 $\frac{2}{9}+\frac{4}{9}+\frac{2}{9}$

Set 3

1 $\frac{1}{2}+\frac{1}{4}$ 2 $\frac{3}{4}+\frac{1}{8}$ 3 $\frac{1}{4}+\frac{3}{8}$

4 $\frac{2}{3}+\frac{1}{6}$ 5 $\frac{2}{5}+\frac{1}{10}$ 6 $\frac{3}{5}+\frac{3}{10}$

7 $\frac{1}{3}+\frac{2}{9}$ 8 $\frac{2}{3}+\frac{1}{9}$ 9 $\frac{1}{2}+\frac{1}{8}$

10 $\frac{1}{2}+\frac{3}{10}$ 11 $\frac{1}{2}+\frac{1}{3}$ 12 $\frac{1}{3}+\frac{1}{4}$

13 $\frac{1}{4}+\frac{2}{3}$ 14 $\frac{1}{4}+\frac{1}{5}$ 15 $\frac{2}{5}+\frac{1}{4}$

FRACTIONS ADDITION (1)

Now try these

Write the answers in their lowest terms

Set 1

1 $\frac{1}{4} + \frac{1}{6}$ **2** $\frac{3}{4} + \frac{1}{6}$ **3** $\frac{1}{6} + \frac{1}{8}$

4 $\frac{1}{4} + \frac{5}{8}$ **5** $\frac{1}{2} + \frac{3}{7}$ **6** $\frac{1}{2} + \frac{1}{5}$

7 $\frac{1}{3} + \frac{1}{5}$ **8** $\frac{1}{12} + \frac{1}{12}$ **9** $\frac{1}{6} + \frac{7}{12}$

10 $\frac{1}{12} + \frac{5}{6}$ **11** $\frac{2}{3} + \frac{1}{6}$ **12** $\frac{1}{3} + \frac{3}{7}$

13 $\frac{2}{9} + \frac{1}{2}$ **14** $\frac{3}{5} + \frac{1}{4}$ **15** $\frac{1}{8} + \frac{1}{16}$

16 $\frac{3}{4} + \frac{3}{16}$ **17** $\frac{1}{2} + \frac{5}{16}$ **18** $\frac{3}{10} + \frac{1}{4}$

19 $\frac{2}{3} + \frac{1}{8}$ **20** $\frac{3}{8} + \frac{1}{12}$ **21** $\frac{1}{6} + \frac{3}{5}$

22 $\frac{3}{4} + \frac{1}{7}$ **23** $\frac{5}{9} + \frac{1}{4}$ **24** $\frac{5}{12} + \frac{1}{9}$

25 $\frac{1}{6} + \frac{5}{9}$ **26** $\frac{3}{10} + \frac{2}{3}$ **27** $\frac{5}{6} + \frac{1}{10}$

Set 2

1 $\frac{1}{3} + \frac{1}{4} + \frac{1}{6}$ **2** $\frac{1}{2} + \frac{1}{5} + \frac{1}{10}$ **3** $\frac{1}{2} + \frac{1}{4} + \frac{1}{8}$

4 $\frac{1}{2} + \frac{1}{8} + \frac{1}{16}$ **5** $\frac{1}{3} + \frac{1}{4} + \frac{1}{8}$ **6** $\frac{1}{12} + \frac{1}{8} + \frac{1}{4}$

7 $\frac{5}{12} + \frac{1}{4} + \frac{1}{6}$ **8** $\frac{1}{4} + \frac{1}{5} + \frac{1}{2}$ **9** $\frac{2}{9} + \frac{1}{12} + \frac{1}{4}$

10 $\frac{1}{2} + \frac{1}{6} + \frac{1}{9}$ **11** $\frac{1}{3} + \frac{1}{5} + \frac{1}{10}$ **12** $\frac{1}{6} + \frac{1}{5} + \frac{1}{3}$

13 $\frac{1}{3} + \frac{1}{6} + \frac{1}{12}$ **14** $\frac{1}{2} + \frac{1}{3} + \frac{1}{8}$ **15** $\frac{2}{5} + \frac{1}{10} + \frac{1}{12}$

FRACTIONS ADDITION (2)

First try these

Write the answers in their lowest terms

Set 1

1 $\frac{3}{4} + \frac{3}{4}$ 2 $\frac{2}{3} + \frac{1}{3}$ 3 $\frac{2}{3} + \frac{2}{3}$

4 $\frac{5}{8} + \frac{3}{8}$ 5 $\frac{7}{8} + \frac{1}{8}$ 6 $\frac{1}{6} + \frac{5}{6}$

7 $\frac{5}{6} + \frac{5}{6}$ 8 $\frac{3}{10} + \frac{7}{10}$ 9 $\frac{3}{4} + \frac{1}{2}$

10 $\frac{3}{4} + \frac{5}{8}$ 11 $\frac{1}{4} + \frac{7}{8}$ 12 $\frac{1}{2} + \frac{7}{8}$

13 $\frac{1}{2} + \frac{2}{3}$ 14 $\frac{3}{4} + \frac{2}{3}$ 15 $\frac{1}{2} + \frac{5}{6}$

16 $\frac{3}{4} + \frac{5}{6}$ 17 $\frac{3}{10} + \frac{4}{5}$ 18 $\frac{7}{12} + \frac{5}{8}$

19 $\frac{1}{2} + \frac{1}{2} + \frac{3}{4}$ 20 $\frac{1}{2} + \frac{3}{5} + \frac{1}{10}$ 21 $\frac{1}{2} + \frac{5}{8} + \frac{3}{16}$

22 $\frac{2}{3} + \frac{1}{4} + \frac{1}{2}$ 23 $\frac{5}{6} + \frac{1}{4} + \frac{1}{3}$ 24 $\frac{7}{12} + \frac{3}{4} + \frac{1}{3}$

Set 2

1 $1\frac{1}{2} + 1\frac{1}{2}$ 2 $1\frac{3}{5} + 1\frac{3}{5}$ 3 $1\frac{1}{2} + \frac{3}{4}$

4 $2\frac{3}{4} + 1\frac{3}{4}$ 5 $1\frac{5}{12} + 2\frac{5}{12}$ 6 $2\frac{3}{8} + 2\frac{3}{8}$

7 $3\frac{1}{8} + 2\frac{3}{16}$ 8 $1\frac{1}{2} + \frac{11}{12}$ 9 $3\frac{7}{12} + \frac{1}{6}$

10 $5\frac{3}{4} + 2\frac{3}{8}$ 11 $6\frac{1}{3} + 2\frac{7}{12}$ 12 $3\frac{1}{2} + \frac{5}{6}$

13 $4\frac{1}{8} + \frac{3}{16}$ 14 $5\frac{3}{16} + 2\frac{1}{4}$ 15 $6\frac{5}{6} + 4\frac{2}{3}$

16 $2\frac{7}{10} + \frac{2}{5}$ 17 $3\frac{7}{8} + 2\frac{3}{4}$ 18 $6\frac{2}{3} + \frac{5}{6}$

19 $5\frac{7}{9} + \frac{2}{3}$ 20 $4\frac{2}{3} + 3\frac{1}{12}$ 21 $1\frac{11}{16} + 2\frac{3}{8}$

FRACTIONS ADDITION (2)

Now try these

Write the answers in their lowest terms

Set 1

1 $\frac{1}{2}+\frac{7}{10}$ **2** $\frac{1}{2}+\frac{3}{5}$ **3** $\frac{4}{5}+\frac{9}{10}$

4 $\frac{1}{6}+\frac{11}{12}$ **5** $\frac{2}{3}+\frac{7}{12}$ **6** $\frac{3}{4}+\frac{5}{12}$

7 $\frac{5}{6}+\frac{2}{9}$ **8** $\frac{7}{16}+\frac{5}{8}$ **9** $\frac{3}{4}+\frac{9}{16}$

10 $\frac{3}{4}+\frac{4}{5}$ **11** $\frac{3}{8}+\frac{5}{6}$ **12** $\frac{7}{8}+\frac{1}{3}$

13 $\frac{5}{8}+\frac{1}{2}+\frac{3}{4}$ **14** $\frac{4}{9}+\frac{2}{3}+\frac{1}{6}$ **15** $\frac{9}{16}+\frac{5}{8}+\frac{1}{4}$

16 $\frac{8}{15}+\frac{1}{5}+\frac{2}{3}$ **17** $\frac{9}{14}+\frac{6}{7}+\frac{1}{2}$ **18** $\frac{5}{12}+\frac{1}{4}+\frac{5}{6}$

Set 2

1 $1\frac{5}{8}+\frac{1}{3}$ **2** $2\frac{5}{8}+4\frac{3}{8}$ **3** $3\frac{7}{8}+2\frac{5}{16}$

4 $4\frac{1}{2}+\frac{1}{12}$ **5** $2\frac{1}{12}+2\frac{5}{6}$ **6** $3\frac{1}{2}+4\frac{5}{6}$

7 $3\frac{5}{8}+2\frac{1}{4}$ **8** $5\frac{2}{3}+2\frac{1}{2}$ **9** $4\frac{3}{10}+3\frac{1}{5}$

10 $3\frac{3}{4}+2\frac{5}{12}$ **11** $5\frac{9}{16}+4\frac{1}{2}$ **12** $3\frac{3}{4}+4\frac{1}{6}$

13 $6\frac{9}{10}+5\frac{4}{5}$ **14** $3\frac{2}{3}+4\frac{1}{4}$ **15** $2\frac{7}{8}+1\frac{1}{12}$

16 $7\frac{2}{15}+3\frac{2}{3}$ **17** $9\frac{3}{8}+2\frac{11}{12}$ **18** $3\frac{7}{15}+8\frac{1}{5}$

19 $4\frac{2}{7}+6\frac{3}{14}$ **20** $5\frac{9}{16}+8\frac{5}{8}$ **21** $6\frac{2}{3}+2\frac{2}{15}$

22 $4\frac{1}{2}+3\frac{1}{4}+\frac{1}{6}$ **23** $2\frac{3}{8}+5\frac{5}{16}+1\frac{3}{4}$

24 $3\frac{7}{10}+1\frac{1}{5}+2\frac{1}{2}$ **25** $4\frac{2}{3}+1\frac{1}{10}+2\frac{5}{6}$

FRACTIONS PROBLEMS

First try these

1 A girl had a book of 104 pages and she had read $\frac{1}{8}$ of it. How many pages had she read?

2 A boy had £16·00, but he spent £2·00 of it. What fraction of his money did he spend?

3 Anne lives $\frac{1}{3}$ of a km from school, and Elizabeth lives $\frac{1}{2}$ km further on. How far from the school does Elizabeth live?

4 Henry was given $\frac{1}{6}$ of a sum of money whilst Mary and John each received one-third. What fraction of the sum of money was given away?

5 By one road it is $\frac{3}{4}$ of a km from our house to the station. By another road it is $1\frac{1}{3}$ km. If I go one way and return the other, how far do I walk altogether?

6 What fraction of 10 m is 2 m?

7 In preparing a cake $4\frac{1}{5}$ kg of dried fruit was added to $3\frac{1}{2}$ kg of flour. What was the total weight of the mixture?

8 In three days we used $\frac{7}{8}$ kg, $1\frac{1}{4}$ kg and $2\frac{5}{8}$ kg of sugar. How much sugar did we use altogether?

9 Find the sum of $6\frac{1}{4}$, $2\frac{1}{3}$ and $4\frac{1}{2}$. Take 3 from the result.

10 What fraction of 1 m is $12\frac{1}{2}$ cm?

11 One-third of a pole was painted black and the remaining 6 m yellow. How many m of the pole were black?

12 A girl gave away $\frac{5}{6}$, and then $\frac{1}{10}$, of her sweets. What fraction of them did she give away altogether?

13 To $\frac{1}{4}$ m was added $\frac{1}{5}$ m. What was the total length? (Answer in cm.)

14 A can holds $1\frac{3}{4}$ litres of petrol and another holds $7\frac{1}{2}$ litres. How much petrol do they hold altogether?

15 A boy spent $\frac{1}{2}$ his money in one shop and $\frac{1}{4}$ in another. He then had 10p left. How much had he to begin with?

16 What fraction of 6 min 40 sec is 1 min 20 sec?

17 Add the sum of $3\frac{3}{4} + 1\frac{1}{3}$ to the sum of $5\frac{1}{6} + 2\frac{1}{2}$.

18 Find the sum of the two smallest of the fractions $\frac{1}{2}, \frac{1}{3}, \frac{1}{4}$; also find the sum of the two largest of these fractions.

FRACTIONS PROBLEMS

Now try these

1 What fraction of 8 litres is 3 half-litres?

2 Five-sevenths of a boy's money was 50p. How much did he have altogether?

3 What fraction of one kg is 375 g?

4 How many $\frac{2}{5}$ litre bottles of milk can be filled from a can holding 6 litres?

5 Joan has a sum of money, and $\frac{1}{3}$ of it is greater than $\frac{1}{6}$ by 25p. How much money has Joan?

6 Add together $\frac{1}{4}$ kg, $\frac{1}{5}$ kg, $\frac{1}{10}$ kg. Give the answer in g.

7 My father is 180 cm tall. I am 4 cm taller than $\frac{2}{3}$ of his height. How tall am I?

8 A room is $4\frac{1}{5}$ m wide and $5\frac{1}{4}$ m long. Find the distance all the way round it.

9 Three-eighths of a park is laid out in gardens and $\frac{2}{5}$ is set aside for games. What fraction of the park is set aside for other purposes?

10 A merchant sold $\frac{1}{2}$, $\frac{1}{4}$ and then $\frac{1}{5}$ of his oil. How many litres had he left out of 160 litres?

11 Add together $\frac{3}{5}$, $\frac{5}{6}$ and $\frac{14}{15}$, and take 2 from the result.

12 A boy is $1\frac{1}{4}$ times as old as his sister. What fraction of the boy's age is his sister's? If the boy is 10 yr old, how old is the sister?

13 If $\frac{3}{4}$ of a quantity of liquid is 30 litres, what is $\frac{7}{8}$ of the same amount?

14 In an orchard $\frac{1}{2}$ of the trees are apple trees, $\frac{1}{6}$ pear trees and the remainder plum trees. There are 30 plum trees. How many apple trees and how many pear trees are there?

15 Smith lifts $\frac{7}{12}$ of 180 kg and Jones lifts $\frac{5}{8}$ of 240 kg. Who lifts the greater amount and by how much?

16 A girl copied down a sum incorrectly, $\frac{1}{2} + \frac{1}{5} + \frac{2}{6}$ instead of $\frac{1}{2} + \frac{2}{5} + \frac{1}{6}$. What was the answer she gave, and what should the answer have been?

17 Add 3 cm to $\frac{3}{10}$ of 3 m.

FRACTIONS SUBTRACTION (1)

First try these

Write the answers in their lowest terms

Set 1

1 $\frac{3}{4} - \frac{1}{4}$ 2 $\frac{5}{8} - \frac{3}{8}$ 3 $\frac{5}{6} - \frac{1}{6}$

4 $\frac{7}{9} - \frac{5}{9}$ 5 $\frac{7}{8} - \frac{1}{2}$ 6 $\frac{5}{8} - \frac{1}{4}$

7 $\frac{5}{6} - \frac{2}{3}$ 8 $\frac{6}{7} - \frac{3}{7}$ 9 $\frac{1}{2} - \frac{1}{6}$

10 $\frac{7}{12} - \frac{1}{3}$ 11 $\frac{8}{9} - \frac{2}{3}$ 12 $\frac{5}{12} - \frac{1}{4}$

13 $\frac{9}{10} - \frac{1}{5}$ 14 $\frac{7}{10} - \frac{2}{5}$ 15 $\frac{11}{12} - \frac{5}{6}$

16 $\frac{7}{9} - \frac{1}{3}$ 17 $\frac{1}{2} - \frac{1}{16}$ 18 $\frac{1}{4} - \frac{3}{16}$

19 $\frac{9}{14} - \frac{2}{7}$ 20 $\frac{5}{8} - \frac{3}{16}$ 21 $\frac{11}{12} - \frac{2}{3}$

22 $\frac{5}{12} - \frac{1}{6}$ 23 $\frac{15}{16} - \frac{1}{4}$ 24 $\frac{13}{15} - \frac{2}{3}$

Set 2

1 $1 - \frac{1}{2}$ 2 $3 - \frac{3}{4}$ 3 $2 - \frac{1}{4}$

4 $4 - \frac{1}{3}$ 5 $2 - \frac{5}{6}$ 6 $5 - 2\frac{2}{3}$

7 $8 - 3\frac{1}{9}$ 8 $6 - 4\frac{3}{8}$ 9 $2\frac{1}{2} - 1\frac{1}{4}$

10 $3\frac{3}{4} - 1\frac{1}{2}$ 11 $4\frac{2}{3} - 1\frac{1}{3}$ 12 $6\frac{7}{8} - 4\frac{3}{8}$

13 $5\frac{5}{8} - 2\frac{1}{2}$ 14 $8\frac{7}{12} - 4\frac{1}{3}$ 15 $7\frac{1}{2} - 1\frac{5}{12}$

16 $4\frac{9}{10} - 2\frac{4}{5}$ 17 $9\frac{1}{3} - 2\frac{1}{6}$ 18 $6\frac{11}{16} - 3\frac{5}{8}$

19 $5\frac{5}{9} - 4\frac{1}{3}$ 20 $8\frac{5}{6} - 1\frac{1}{12}$ 21 $8\frac{2}{5} - 1\frac{3}{10}$

FRACTIONS SUBTRACTION (1)

Now try these

Write the answers in their lowest terms

Set 1

1 $\frac{3}{4} - \frac{1}{2}$ 2 $\frac{2}{3} - \frac{1}{4}$ 3 $\frac{1}{2} - \frac{2}{5}$

4 $\frac{5}{6} - \frac{3}{4}$ 5 $\frac{3}{4} - \frac{2}{3}$ 6 $\frac{2}{3} - \frac{1}{2}$

7 $\frac{1}{4} - \frac{1}{6}$ 8 $\frac{3}{4} - \frac{1}{6}$ 9 $\frac{1}{6} - \frac{1}{8}$

10 $\frac{1}{2} - \frac{3}{7}$ 11 $\frac{1}{3} - \frac{1}{5}$ 12 $\frac{7}{9} - \frac{1}{2}$

13 $\frac{7}{10} - \frac{1}{4}$ 14 $\frac{2}{3} - \frac{1}{8}$ 15 $\frac{5}{8} - \frac{5}{12}$

16 $\frac{4}{5} - \frac{1}{2}$ 17 $\frac{8}{9} - \frac{5}{6}$ 18 $\frac{15}{16} - \frac{3}{8}$

19 $\frac{4}{9} - \frac{1}{6}$ 20 $\frac{4}{5} - \frac{2}{3}$ 21 $\frac{5}{6} - \frac{3}{10}$

22 $\frac{9}{10} - \frac{3}{4}$ 23 $\frac{3}{4} - \frac{1}{16}$ 24 $\frac{7}{12} - \frac{1}{3}$

Set 2

1 $2 - \frac{2}{3}$ 2 $4 - \frac{7}{12}$ 3 $3 - \frac{7}{8}$

4 $1 - \frac{2}{9}$ 5 $4\frac{2}{3} - 1\frac{1}{2}$ 6 $8\frac{3}{4} - 2\frac{1}{8}$

7 $5\frac{3}{4} - 1\frac{2}{3}$ 8 $3\frac{3}{5} - \frac{1}{2}$ 9 $9\frac{3}{4} - 1\frac{9}{16}$

10 $2\frac{2}{3} - \frac{3}{8}$ 11 $10\frac{1}{3} - 4\frac{1}{5}$ 12 $7\frac{7}{8} - 3\frac{3}{4}$

13 $3\frac{7}{9} - 2\frac{2}{3}$ 14 $9\frac{7}{10} - 7\frac{1}{2}$ 15 $6\frac{11}{12} - 2\frac{1}{6}$

16 $4\frac{3}{4} - 1\frac{5}{12}$ 17 $5\frac{13}{15} - 1\frac{7}{10}$ 18 $3\frac{4}{5} - 2\frac{1}{10}$

19 $5\frac{7}{9} - \frac{5}{18}$ 20 $10\frac{4}{9} - 3\frac{1}{6}$ 21 $11\frac{7}{8} - 1\frac{5}{12}$

FRACTIONS SUBTRACTION (2)

First try these

Write the answers in their lowest terms

Set 1

1 $3\frac{1}{6} - 1\frac{5}{6}$ **2** $5\frac{3}{8} - 2\frac{7}{8}$ **3** $6\frac{2}{5} - \frac{4}{5}$

4 $8\frac{1}{3} - 3\frac{2}{3}$ **5** $2\frac{1}{4} - \frac{1}{2}$ **6** $4\frac{1}{2} - 1\frac{3}{4}$

7 $1\frac{1}{4} - \frac{3}{4}$ **8** $5\frac{1}{8} - 3\frac{1}{4}$ **9** $4\frac{1}{4} - 2\frac{3}{8}$

10 $6\frac{1}{2} - 3\frac{5}{8}$ **11** $7\frac{3}{4} - \frac{7}{8}$ **12** $5\frac{3}{8} - \frac{3}{4}$

13 $2\frac{1}{8} - \frac{1}{2}$ **14** $3\frac{1}{6} - 2\frac{1}{2}$ **15** $5\frac{1}{6} - 4\frac{1}{3}$

16 $6\frac{2}{3} - \frac{5}{6}$ **17** $4\frac{1}{3} - 1\frac{1}{2}$ **18** $9\frac{1}{6} - 5\frac{5}{12}$

19 $10\frac{2}{3} - 3\frac{11}{12}$ **20** $8\frac{1}{4} - 1\frac{7}{12}$ **21** $6\frac{1}{2} - 4\frac{11}{12}$

22 $7\frac{1}{3} - \frac{5}{12}$ **23** $8\frac{5}{12} - 6\frac{3}{4}$ **24** $9\frac{3}{8} - 1\frac{9}{16}$

Set 2

1 $3 + 2\frac{1}{2} - 1\frac{1}{4}$ **2** $5\frac{1}{3} + 1\frac{1}{2} - 2\frac{5}{6}$

3 $5\frac{1}{4} - \frac{1}{8} + 2\frac{1}{2}$ **4** $4\frac{1}{2} - 5\frac{3}{4} + 6\frac{1}{3}$

5 $6\frac{7}{16} + 2\frac{3}{8} - 4\frac{3}{4}$ **6** $3\frac{3}{5} - 4 + 6\frac{3}{10}$

7 $4\frac{1}{3} + 7 - 1\frac{1}{12}$ **8** $8\frac{2}{3} - 10\frac{5}{9} + 5\frac{2}{3}$

9 $7\frac{1}{4} - 2\frac{7}{8} - 1\frac{1}{2}$ **10** $4\frac{7}{12} - 3\frac{3}{4} + 5\frac{1}{2}$

11 $\frac{2}{3} + 7\frac{5}{6} + 5\frac{1}{6}$ **12** $3\frac{3}{4} + \frac{1}{12} + 2\frac{5}{6}$

FRACTIONS SUBTRACTION (2)

Now try these

Write the answers in their lowest terms

Set 1

1 $2\frac{1}{8} - \frac{7}{8}$ **2** $5\frac{1}{4} - 3\frac{5}{8}$ **3** $6\frac{3}{8} - 1\frac{7}{16}$

4 $3\frac{1}{5} - 1\frac{7}{10}$ **5** $4\frac{3}{4} - 1\frac{13}{16}$ **6** $5\frac{1}{2} - 2\frac{11}{16}$

7 $6\frac{5}{12} - 4\frac{1}{2}$ **8** $7\frac{1}{4} - \frac{7}{16}$ **9** $6\frac{2}{5} - 2\frac{9}{10}$

10 $4\frac{1}{10} - 1\frac{1}{5}$ **11** $8\frac{7}{10} - \frac{4}{5}$ **12** $9\frac{2}{3} - 1\frac{3}{4}$

13 $8\frac{1}{3} - 2\frac{3}{4}$ **14** $10\frac{1}{4} - 9\frac{1}{3}$ **15** $11\frac{1}{2} - 3\frac{3}{5}$

16 $6\frac{1}{5} - 2\frac{1}{4}$ **17** $3\frac{3}{10} - \frac{1}{2}$ **18** $7\frac{1}{10} - 2\frac{3}{4}$

19 $8\frac{1}{8} - 3\frac{1}{3}$ **20** $9\frac{3}{8} - 1\frac{2}{3}$ **21** $9\frac{1}{8} - 3\frac{1}{6}$

22 $10\frac{5}{8} - 4\frac{5}{6}$ **23** $6\frac{1}{5} - 5\frac{2}{3}$ **24** $8\frac{1}{3} - 1\frac{4}{5}$

Set 2

1 $\frac{3}{4} + \frac{5}{6} + \frac{7}{12}$ **2** $\frac{5}{16} - \frac{3}{4} + \frac{7}{8}$

3 $2\frac{3}{4} + 5\frac{1}{2} - 7\frac{1}{8}$ **4** $3\frac{5}{12} - 1\frac{1}{3} + 6\frac{1}{4}$

5 $7\frac{3}{5} + 2\frac{1}{2} - \frac{3}{10}$ **6** $8\frac{2}{3} - 4\frac{5}{9} - \frac{1}{9}$

7 $5\frac{1}{2} + 3\frac{2}{3} - 6\frac{3}{4}$ **8** $4 + \frac{7}{16} + 1\frac{3}{8}$

9 $6\frac{2}{3} + 4\frac{1}{4} - 2\frac{1}{2}$ **10** $\frac{11}{12} - 4\frac{1}{2} + 10\frac{3}{4}$

11 $3\frac{7}{15} + 8\frac{1}{3} + 9\frac{1}{5}$ **12** $7\frac{3}{16} + 2\frac{1}{2} - 5\frac{1}{8}$

FRACTIONS PROBLEMS

First try these

1 The winner of a race took $10\frac{3}{5}$ sec and the second man took $11\frac{1}{5}$ sec. What was the difference in their times?

2 A girl had 60p. She spent $\frac{1}{2}$ of it on Monday and $\frac{1}{3}$ of it on Tuesday. How much more did she spend on Monday than on Tuesday? Give the answer (a) as a fraction, and (b) in pence.

3 Find the sum of $2\frac{1}{2}$ cm, $3\frac{3}{4}$ cm and $1\frac{1}{8}$ cm. By how much is your result short of 1 m?

4 Ann used to live $3\frac{1}{8}$ km from the railway station, but now she lives only $1\frac{3}{4}$ km away. How much nearer is she now to the station?

5 A small tank holds 54 litres of water. A dozen men each take 6 half-litres. What fraction of the water remains?

6 A man pays $\frac{1}{8}$ of his wages in rent and $\frac{1}{12}$ in taxes. How much more does he pay in rent than in taxes?

7 There are 128 children in a school and $\frac{9}{16}$ of them are girls. What fraction of the pupils are boys? How many boys are there?

8 (a) What fraction of 1 kg is 200 g? (b) From 75 cm take 15 cm, and express your answer as a fraction of 1 m.

9 A packet of oats weighs $\frac{1}{2}$ kg. If the empty packet weighs $\frac{1}{8}$ kg, find what weight of oats is in the packet. Give the answer (a) as a fraction of a kg, and (b) in g.

10 What must be added to $3\frac{5}{9}$ to make it equal to the sum of $1\frac{1}{2}$ and $3\frac{1}{6}$?

11 A man is laying a garden path, which is to be $9\frac{1}{4}$ m long. So far he has laid $4\frac{2}{3}$ m. What length of path has still to be made? Answer in m as a mixed number.

12 Which is the greatest, and which is the least of these fractions: $\frac{11}{12}$, $\frac{3}{4}$, $\frac{5}{6}$? Subtract the greatest from 2.

13 John walks for $1\frac{1}{4}$ h and Susan walks for $\frac{7}{12}$ h. Who walks for the longer time and by how much?

14 The sum of two numbers is $\frac{8}{15}$. If one of them is $\frac{1}{3}$, find the other.

FRACTIONS PROBLEMS

Now try these

1 The sum of two numbers is $8\frac{1}{2}$. If one of the numbers is $1\frac{3}{5}$, find the other.

2 A boy gave $\frac{1}{4}$ of his sweets to his brother and $\frac{1}{3}$ to his sister. What fraction of his sweets did he keep for himself?

3 Take $\frac{3}{4}$ from $6\frac{5}{8}$, and then subtract $1\frac{7}{8}$ from the result.

4 Alan went on a journey of 108 km. He travelled $\frac{5}{9}$ of the way by train and went one-half of the remainder by bus, and the other half by cycle. Find (a) what fraction of the journey he cycled, and (b) the distance cycled, in km.

5 Find the value of one half of $\frac{4}{5}$ of 10 litres.

6 Of 120 kg of potatoes one-eighth was diseased, and $\frac{5}{6}$ were sold. What weight of the potatoes remained?

7 Write down the following fractions in order of size with the largest on the left and the smallest on the right: $\frac{1}{3}, \frac{1}{7}, \frac{1}{5}, \frac{1}{9}, \frac{1}{2}, \frac{1}{6}$. Take the smallest from the largest.

8 From a piece of metal $8\frac{1}{4}$ cm long a piece $5\frac{1}{10}$ cm was cut. What length of metal remained?

9 From a length of rope $30\frac{1}{2}$ m long three pieces were cut. The lengths were $6\frac{1}{8}$ m, $3\frac{3}{5}$ m and $7\frac{1}{4}$ m. What length of rope remained? Give the answer (a) in m, as a mixed number, and (b) in cm.

10 Three-fifths of my money is greater than $\frac{1}{4}$ of it by 70p. How much money have I?

11 From $\frac{3}{4}$ kg take $\frac{7}{10}$ kg. Give the answer (a) as a fraction of a kg, and (b) in g.

12 To the sum of $\frac{1}{3}$ and $\frac{1}{5}$ add the difference between $\frac{1}{3}$ and $\frac{1}{5}$.

13 What fraction of £1·00 is left after spending $\frac{1}{4}$ of it in one shop and $\frac{3}{8}$ of it in another?

14 If $2\frac{3}{10}$ m of a 10 m pole is painted red, $1\frac{1}{4}$ m white, and the remainder in blue, what length is blue? Give the answer in metres and as a fraction of a metre.

GENERAL REVISION

First try these

Add

1   7729
          8
  +9463
———

2 £
    $5 \cdot 47\frac{1}{2}$
  $72 \cdot 53$
  $+ \cdot 89$
———

3 $7\frac{1}{6} + 2\frac{1}{4}$

Subtract

4 kg g
  140 97
 − 85 478
———

5 $16\frac{1}{2} - 9\frac{7}{10}$

6 km m
  31 160
 − 2 310
———

Multiply

7 h min
  10 25
    × 2
———

8 litres ml
    7 498
    × 2
———

9 m cm
  7 10
   × 2
———

Divide

10 £
  $9)109 \cdot 65$

11 m cm
  $2)$ 9 68

12 $18)757$

13 Write in figures twenty-five thousand and fourteen.

14 Change 2500 ml to half-litres.

15 What is the cost of half a dozen articles at £9·35 each?

16 Of 480 people present at a concert $\frac{3}{16}$ were boys and $\frac{5}{16}$ were girls. The rest were adults. How many boys were present, and how many girls?

17 Find the cost of 8 kg at 18p per 250 g.

18 From 10 003 take 9097.

19 A ball of string contains 50 m. If 23 lengths each measuring 35 cm are cut off, how much string is left? (Answer in m and cm.)

20 What is the cost of 13 articles at £16·42 for two?

21 Find the difference between $\frac{4}{5}$ of £2·50 and $\frac{3}{8}$ of £4·80.

22 The sum of £39·60 was increased by $\frac{1}{6}$. What was the sum of money then?

GENERAL REVISION

Now try these

Add

1
kg	g
57	390
14	762
+	908

2
litres	ml
64	253
1	29
+49	874

3 $9\frac{5}{6} + \frac{1}{10} + \frac{2}{5}$

Subtract

4
47 003
− 28 109

5
km	m
21	504
− 6	728

6 $5\frac{5}{9} - 2\frac{1}{3} - 1\frac{1}{2}$

Multiply

7
£
8·12½
×9

8
m	cm
16	57
×2	

9
307
×29

Divide

10 $1\frac{1}{2}$ kg ÷ 2   **11** 39 litres ÷ 2   **12** 80)7490

13 Write in figures fifty-one thousand seven hundred and seven.

14 A man travelled $\frac{5}{16}$ of a journey by air, $\frac{7}{20}$ by sea and the remainder by train. What fraction of the journey did he make by train?

15 A full truck weighs 18 750 kg, and the empty truck weighs 8250 kg. Find the value of the load in the truck if it costs £0·08 per kg.

16 Fifty metres of material is cut into ten pieces of equal length and each piece is long enough to make two aprons. What length is needed for one apron?

17 A boy cycles three times as fast as he can walk. He walks at the rate of $3\frac{1}{2}$ km/h. How long will he take to cycle 21 km?

18 Half the weight of a cart is one-third the weight of a light lorry. The lorry weighs 750 kg. What is the weight of the cart?

FRACTIONS MULTIPLICATION (1)

First try these

Set 1

1 $\frac{1}{2} \times 2$ 2 $\frac{2}{3} \times 3$ 3 $\frac{3}{4} \times 4$

4 $\frac{2}{5} \times 5$ 5 $\frac{7}{8} \times 8$ 6 $\frac{3}{10} \times 10$

7 $\frac{5}{7} \times 7$ 8 $\frac{4}{9} \times 9$ 9 $\frac{1}{2} \times \frac{2}{5}$

10 $\frac{1}{4} \times \frac{4}{7}$ 11 $\frac{1}{3} \times \frac{3}{10}$ 12 $\frac{2}{3} \times \frac{1}{2}$

13 $\frac{1}{4} \times \frac{4}{5}$ 14 $\frac{1}{5} \times \frac{5}{12}$ 15 $\frac{3}{8} \times \frac{1}{3}$

16 $\frac{7}{10} \times \frac{1}{7}$ 17 $\frac{5}{8} \times \frac{1}{5}$ 18 $\frac{7}{9} \times \frac{9}{10}$

19 $\frac{3}{4} \times \frac{4}{5}$ 20 $\frac{8}{9} \times \frac{1}{8}$ 21 $\frac{1}{10} \times \frac{10}{11}$

Set 2

1 $\frac{3}{4} \times 2$ 2 $\frac{2}{5} \times 10$ 3 $\frac{5}{16} \times 8$

4 $\frac{2}{9} \times 3$ 5 $\frac{4}{15} \times 5$ 6 $\frac{5}{8} \times 16$

7 $\frac{1}{12} \times 4$ 8 $\frac{3}{10} \times 5$ 9 $\frac{1}{2} \times \frac{4}{7}$

10 $\frac{2}{3} \times \frac{1}{8}$ 11 $\frac{1}{3} \times \frac{6}{7}$ 12 $\frac{2}{3} \times \frac{5}{6}$

13 $\frac{1}{4} \times \frac{8}{9}$ 14 $\frac{4}{5} \times \frac{1}{16}$ 15 $\frac{1}{10} \times \frac{5}{8}$

16 $\frac{3}{4} \times \frac{1}{9}$ 17 $\frac{1}{3} \times \frac{9}{10}$ 18 $\frac{2}{3} \times \frac{1}{4}$

19 $\frac{3}{4} \times \frac{1}{12}$ 20 $\frac{2}{9} \times \frac{3}{5}$ 21 $\frac{6}{7} \times \frac{2}{3}$

FRACTIONS MULTIPLICATION (1)

Now try these

Set 1

1 $\frac{5}{6} \times 6$

2 $\frac{3}{7} \times 7$

3 $\frac{11}{12} \times 12$

4 $\frac{3}{16} \times 16$

5 $\frac{7}{15} \times 15$

6 $\frac{9}{10} \times 10$

7 $\frac{1}{12} \times 12$

8 $\frac{5}{8} \times 8$

9 $\frac{1}{3} \times \frac{3}{4}$

10 $\frac{4}{5} \times \frac{5}{9}$

11 $\frac{1}{7} \times \frac{7}{10}$

12 $\frac{5}{16} \times \frac{1}{5}$

13 $\frac{7}{8} \times \frac{5}{7}$

14 $\frac{11}{16} \times \frac{9}{11}$

15 $\frac{7}{12} \times \frac{1}{7}$

16 $\frac{2}{15} \times \frac{1}{2}$

17 $\frac{7}{9} \times \frac{9}{16}$

18 $\frac{4}{7} \times \frac{1}{4}$

19 $\frac{7}{11} \times \frac{11}{12}$

20 $\frac{13}{15} \times \frac{15}{16}$

21 $\frac{11}{16} \times \frac{5}{11}$

Set 2

1 $\frac{3}{16} \times 4$

2 $\frac{5}{24} \times 8$

3 $\frac{1}{6} \times 18$

4 $\frac{4}{15} \times 5$

5 $\frac{7}{12} \times 24$

6 $\frac{9}{16} \times 8$

7 $\frac{3}{11} \times 22$

8 $\frac{6}{7} \times 21$

9 $\frac{1}{15} \times \frac{3}{10}$

10 $\frac{7}{10} \times \frac{5}{6}$

11 $\frac{2}{3} \times \frac{7}{12}$

12 $\frac{4}{9} \times \frac{3}{5}$

13 $\frac{8}{15} \times \frac{1}{4}$

14 $\frac{9}{11} \times \frac{2}{3}$

15 $\frac{12}{13} \times \frac{3}{4}$

16 $\frac{14}{15} \times \frac{2}{7}$

17 $\frac{1}{12} \times \frac{4}{5}$

18 $\frac{13}{18} \times \frac{9}{10}$

19 $\frac{15}{16} \times \frac{3}{5}$

20 $\frac{17}{20} \times \frac{5}{8}$

21 $\frac{7}{11} \times \frac{22}{35}$

FRACTIONS MULTIPLICATION (2)

First try these

Set 1

1 $\frac{2}{3} \times \frac{3}{4}$ 2 $\frac{7}{8} \times \frac{2}{7}$ 3 $\frac{4}{5} \times \frac{5}{8}$

4 $\frac{2}{3} \times \frac{9}{10}$ 5 $\frac{3}{5} \times \frac{5}{12}$ 6 $\frac{6}{7} \times \frac{7}{12}$

7 $\frac{2}{9} \times \frac{3}{8}$ 8 $\frac{5}{16} \times \frac{8}{15}$ 9 $\frac{4}{5} \times \frac{9}{10}$

10 $\frac{7}{10} \times \frac{8}{14}$ 11 $\frac{8}{15} \times \frac{5}{10}$ 12 $\frac{8}{27} \times \frac{9}{20}$

13 $\frac{9}{20}$ of $\frac{10}{21}$ 14 $\frac{8}{33}$ of $\frac{11}{12}$ 15 $\frac{13}{24}$ of $\frac{15}{26}$

16 $\frac{15}{28}$ of $\frac{21}{25}$ 17 $\frac{11}{20} \times \frac{5}{22}$ 18 $\frac{9}{14}$ of $\frac{7}{15}$

Set 2

1 $9 \times 1\frac{1}{6}$ 2 $12 \times 4\frac{1}{3}$ 3 $10 \times 2\frac{1}{2}$

4 $1\frac{1}{2} \times 1\frac{1}{3}$ 5 $\frac{3}{4}$ of $2\frac{2}{3}$ 6 $\frac{3}{16} \times 1\frac{1}{15}$

7 $\frac{1}{11}$ of $8\frac{1}{4}$ 8 $\frac{4}{15}$ of $6\frac{2}{3}$ 9 $1\frac{3}{4}$ of $4\frac{1}{7}$

10 $3\frac{1}{3} \times 4\frac{1}{5}$ 11 $2\frac{2}{9} \times 1\frac{1}{2}$ 12 $5\frac{1}{2} \times 2\frac{4}{11}$

13 $2\frac{1}{10} \times 2\frac{2}{9}$ 14 $6\frac{3}{4}$ of $1\frac{1}{3}$ 15 $7\frac{1}{2} \times 3\frac{3}{5}$

16 $3\frac{3}{5} \times 1\frac{2}{3}$ 17 $5\frac{1}{3} \times 6\frac{3}{4}$ 18 $1\frac{3}{8} \times 2\frac{2}{11}$

19 $4\frac{4}{5} \times 6\frac{1}{4}$ 20 $3\frac{1}{6} \times 2\frac{2}{5}$ 21 $1\frac{1}{6}$ of $1\frac{1}{7}$

22 $5\frac{1}{3} \times 1\frac{5}{16}$ 23 $2\frac{1}{7} \times 9\frac{4}{5}$ 24 $4\frac{3}{4}$ of $2\frac{2}{7}$

FRACTIONS MULTIPLICATION (2)

Now try these

Set 1

1 $\frac{5}{12} \times \frac{4}{5}$ **2** $\frac{7}{10} \times \frac{25}{28}$ **3** $\frac{9}{16} \times \frac{8}{15}$

4 $\frac{7}{8} \times \frac{6}{7}$ **5** $\frac{7}{12} \times \frac{16}{21}$ **6** $\frac{8}{15} \times \frac{5}{12}$

7 $\frac{16}{25} \times \frac{15}{32}$ **8** $\frac{9}{16} \times \frac{8}{27}$ **9** $\frac{11}{12} \times \frac{3}{22}$

10 $\frac{7}{20} \times \frac{5}{21}$ **11** $\frac{4}{15} \times \frac{5}{16}$ **12** $\frac{20}{33} \times \frac{11}{16}$

13 $\frac{18}{25}$ of $\frac{10}{27}$ **14** $\frac{15}{44}$ of $\frac{11}{25}$ **15** $\frac{7}{18}$ of $\frac{9}{28}$

16 $\frac{16}{35}$ of $\frac{15}{32}$ **17** $\frac{17}{36} \times \frac{9}{34}$ **18** $\frac{13}{44}$ of $\frac{11}{39}$

Set 2

1 $15 \times 1\frac{1}{5}$ **2** $20 \times 2\frac{3}{10}$ **3** $18 \times 3\frac{1}{6}$

4 $24 \times 1\frac{5}{8}$ **5** $\frac{4}{5}$ of $8\frac{3}{4}$ **6** $\frac{11}{16}$ of $2\frac{10}{11}$

7 $\frac{7}{12}$ of $4\frac{4}{5}$ **8** $\frac{8}{15}$ of $9\frac{3}{8}$ **9** $7\frac{1}{2} \times 3\frac{1}{5}$

10 $5\frac{1}{3}$ of $1\frac{11}{16}$ **11** $5\frac{5}{8} \times 3\frac{5}{9}$ **12** $3\frac{3}{4} \times 6\frac{2}{5}$

13 $10\frac{2}{5}$ of $1\frac{2}{13}$ **14** $6\frac{2}{9} \times 2\frac{5}{8}$ **15** $9\frac{2}{7} \times 2\frac{2}{13}$

16 $4\frac{7}{12} \times 2\frac{4}{11}$ **17** $3\frac{5}{16} \times 1\frac{3}{5}$ **18** $3\frac{3}{8} \times 7\frac{1}{9}$

19 $7\frac{1}{7} \times 9\frac{1}{10}$ **20** $5\frac{1}{11}$ of $3\frac{2}{3}$ **21** $2\frac{13}{16} \times 3\frac{7}{15}$

22 $4\frac{2}{3} \times 8\frac{1}{4}$ **23** $7\frac{1}{12}$ of $7\frac{1}{5}$ **24** $10\frac{2}{7} \times 1\frac{1}{6}$

GENERAL REVISION

First try these

Add

1
```
   9742
   4825
 + 8219
 ──────
```

2
kg	m
3	200
14	805
+	880

3
weeks	days	h
9	3	17
2	5	14
+ 1	2	20

Subtract

4 $14\frac{7}{12} - 2\frac{3}{8}$

5
tonnes	kg
16	106
− 12	98

6
kg	g
12	305
− 6	840

Multiply

7
m	cm
20	51
	× 2

8 $2\frac{1}{7} \times 1\frac{3}{4}$

9 $10\frac{1}{2} \times 4\frac{1}{3}$

Divide

10 $24\overline{)985}$

11
min	sec
2)33	15

12
litres	ml
2) 21	492

13 Write in figures eight thousand one hundred and five.

14 Joan saved 2p every day, Sundays included. How much did she save in a year?

15 Last year a housewife bought a tonne of material for £14·50. This year it is 15p a 100 kg dearer. What will she now pay for a tonne of the material?

16 Nine kg of sweets were weighed out into 60 g packets. How many packets were there?

17 Multiply the sum of $3\frac{1}{2}$ and $2\frac{1}{3}$ by $1\frac{1}{7}$.

18 Divide the difference between 18 litres and 7 litres 500 ml by 2.

19 By how much is 412 cm less than $4\frac{1}{2}$ m?

20 How many minutes are there between 11:29 and 12:06?

21 How many objects each weighing 30 g together weigh 12 kg?

22 Find the value of $\frac{7}{8}$ of £1·00 × $\frac{3}{4}$ of £5·00.

GENERAL REVISION

Now try these

Add

1	£
	45·47½
	122·39
	+ 0·24

2	tonnes	kg
	18	130
	17	925
	+ 20	8

3	m	cm
	33	23
	15	30
	+ 46	87

Subtract

4	£
	295·40
	– 168·93

5	35 002
	– 19 670

6	m	cm
	16	76
	– 9	89

Multiply

7	km	m
	17	980
		× 2

8 $11\frac{1}{4} \times 6\frac{2}{5}$

9	m	cm
	15	22
		× 7

Divide

10 £ 12)55·20

11 kg g 2)29 310

12 59)2000

13 Write in figures eighty-six thousand and two.

14 A piece of metal $6\frac{2}{5}$ cm long was joined to another $7\frac{3}{10}$ cm long. Allowing for a loss of $1\frac{1}{2}$ cm in joining, what was the total length of the new piece of metal?

15 The rent of a house is £8·50 per week. What rent is paid in 1 year?

16 A jet aeroplane travels at 960 km/h. How far does it travel in 1 sec? (Answer in m.)

17 Mary received $\frac{9}{16}$ of her aunt's money and Susan received $\frac{1}{6}$ as much as Mary. If her aunt had £1280·00, how much did each girl receive?

18 What is the smallest number that must be subtracted from 895 to make it exactly divisible by 19?

19 What is the total weight of cement in 10 loads, if one load is 5 tonnes 350 kg?

FRACTIONS DIVISION

First try these

Set 1

1 $6 \div 3$ **2** $3 \div 6$ **3** $8 \div 4$

4 $4 \div 8$ **5** $6 \div 4$ **6** $4 \div 6$

7 $12 \div 9$ **8** $9 \div 12$ **9** $18 \div 6$

10 $6 \div 18$ **11** $25 \div 5$ **12** $5 \div 25$

13 $7 \div 4$ **14** $4 \div 7$ **15** $3 \div 12$

Set 2

1 $6\frac{1}{2} \div 2$ **2** $1\frac{1}{2} \div 3$ **3** $7\frac{1}{2} \div 5$

4 $9\frac{1}{2} \div 2$ **5** $8\frac{1}{2} \div 4$ **6** $1\frac{1}{4} \div 5$

7 $1\frac{1}{6} \div 7$ **8** $2\frac{1}{4} \div 9$ **9** $4\frac{1}{2} \div 3$

10 $10\frac{1}{2} \div 7$ **11** $4\frac{4}{5} \div 6$ **12** $10\frac{2}{3} \div 8$

13 $\frac{1}{2} \div 3$ **14** $\frac{1}{4} \div 2$ **15** $\frac{2}{3} \div 4$

16 $\frac{3}{5} \div 6$ **17** $\frac{5}{6} \div 5$ **18** $\frac{4}{5} \div 2$

19 $\frac{3}{8} \div 3$ **20** $\frac{7}{10} \div 7$ **21** $\frac{5}{9} \div 10$

22 $\frac{9}{16} \div 3$ **23** $\frac{15}{16} \div 5$ **24** $\frac{5}{12} \div 10$

25 $\frac{2}{3} \div \frac{4}{9}$ **26** $\frac{4}{5} \div \frac{7}{10}$ **27** $\frac{3}{4} \div \frac{5}{8}$

FRACTIONS DIVISION

Now try these

Set 1

1 $12 \div 4$ **2** $4 \div 12$ **3** $20 \div 5$

4 $5 \div 20$ **5** $30 \div 6$ **6** $6 \div 30$

7 $21 \div 6$ **8** $6 \div 21$ **9** $3\frac{1}{2} \div 2$

10 $4\frac{1}{2} \div 9$ **11** $5\frac{1}{4} \div 7$ **12** $2\frac{1}{7} \div 15$

13 $1\frac{1}{9} \div 10$ **14** $2\frac{2}{3} \div 12$ **15** $5\frac{1}{3} \div 8$

Set 2

1 $\frac{1}{3} \div 2$ **2** $\frac{3}{4} \div 3$ **3** $\frac{4}{9} \div 8$

4 $\frac{5}{8} \div 15$ **5** $\frac{7}{8} \div 14$ **6** $\frac{3}{4} \div \frac{5}{12}$

7 $\frac{9}{16} \div \frac{3}{4}$ **8** $\frac{5}{9} \div \frac{2}{3}$ **9** $\frac{5}{6} \div \frac{1}{8}$

10 $\frac{2}{3} \div \frac{7}{12}$ **11** $\frac{8}{15} \div \frac{8}{9}$ **12** $\frac{9}{14} \div \frac{3}{7}$

13 $\frac{5}{18} \div \frac{10}{27}$ **14** $\frac{4}{9} \div \frac{8}{15}$ **15** $\frac{5}{16} \div \frac{3}{8}$

16 $\frac{7}{11} \div \frac{3}{22}$ **17** $3\frac{1}{2} \div 1\frac{3}{4}$ **18** $4\frac{1}{3} \div 3\frac{1}{4}$

19 $2\frac{2}{9} \div 5\frac{1}{3}$ **20** $4\frac{1}{2} \div 3\frac{3}{4}$ **21** $5\frac{1}{4} \div 2\frac{1}{3}$

22 $4\frac{1}{6} \div 6\frac{2}{3}$ **23** $3\frac{1}{9} \div 1\frac{7}{9}$ **24** $8\frac{1}{3} \div 2\frac{2}{9}$

25 $5\frac{2}{5} \div 4\frac{1}{2}$ **26** $5\frac{3}{7} \div 9\frac{1}{2}$ **27** $2\frac{11}{12} \div 8\frac{3}{4}$

FRACTIONS MULTIPLICATION AND DIVISION

First try these

Set 1

1 $\frac{1}{4} \div \frac{2}{5}$ **2** $\frac{2}{3} \div \frac{1}{12}$ **3** $28 \div \frac{7}{20}$

4 $\frac{4}{11} \div \frac{3}{22}$ **5** $2\frac{3}{4} \div 4\frac{1}{2}$ **6** $3\frac{1}{2} \div 1\frac{1}{13}$

7 $\frac{2}{3} \div 1\frac{1}{9}$ **8** $\frac{5}{6} \div 10$ **9** $1\frac{3}{5} \div 8$

10 $\frac{3}{10} \div 6$ **11** $\frac{8}{9} \div \frac{1}{6}$ **12** $1\frac{1}{5} \div \frac{3}{10}$

13 $14 \div 4\frac{2}{3}$ **14** $\frac{8}{15} \div \frac{1}{5}$ **15** $\frac{11}{12} \div \frac{1}{18}$

16 $2\frac{2}{7} \div \frac{4}{7}$ **17** $3\frac{3}{5} \div 1\frac{1}{2}$ **18** $4\frac{1}{8} \div 2\frac{1}{4}$

19 $\frac{11}{16} \div 22$ **20** $\frac{14}{15} \div 4\frac{1}{5}$ **21** $5\frac{3}{4} \div 6\frac{4}{7}$

Set 2

1 $(\frac{2}{3}$ of $15) \div 5$ **2** $(4 \times \frac{5}{8}) \div \frac{2}{5}$

3 $(1\frac{1}{9}$ of $1\frac{1}{2}) \div 4$ **4** $(2\frac{1}{4} \times 8) \div 3$

5 $(\frac{3}{5}$ of $\frac{7}{9}) \div 3\frac{1}{2}$ **6** $(\frac{4}{9} \times \frac{6}{7}) \div 2\frac{1}{7}$

7 $(1\frac{1}{5} \times 2\frac{1}{2}) \div \frac{3}{4}$ **8** $(\frac{5}{16}$ of $3\frac{1}{3}) \div 1\frac{1}{4}$

9 $(\frac{1}{3}$ of $\frac{9}{10}) \div 1\frac{2}{3}$ **10** $(\frac{7}{16} \times \frac{4}{9}) \div 1\frac{3}{4}$

11 $(9 \times 6\frac{2}{3}) \div 1\frac{7}{8}$ **12** $(2\frac{2}{5}$ of $\frac{1}{6}) \div 4$

13 $(2\frac{3}{4}$ of $1\frac{1}{2}) \div 1\frac{3}{8}$ **14** $5\frac{1}{4} \div (4\frac{2}{3}$ of $\frac{1}{2})$

FRACTIONS MULTIPLICATION AND DIVISION

Now try these

Set 1

1 $5\frac{3}{5} \div 2\frac{4}{5}$ **2** $3\frac{3}{8} \div 2\frac{1}{4}$ **3** $\frac{7}{16} \div 3\frac{1}{2}$

4 $\frac{4}{5} \div 1\frac{4}{15}$ **5** $6\frac{2}{7} \div 1\frac{4}{7}$ **6** $6\frac{3}{4} \div 2\frac{5}{8}$

7 $2\frac{5}{14} \div 2\frac{2}{21}$ **8** $\frac{17}{18} \div 3\frac{2}{5}$ **9** $8\frac{3}{4} \div \frac{7}{10}$

10 $3\frac{1}{4} \div 2\frac{1}{3}$ **11** $1\frac{1}{20} \div \frac{7}{48}$ **12** $\frac{5}{18} \div 5\frac{5}{6}$

13 $10\frac{2}{3} \div 3\frac{1}{3}$ **14** $4\frac{1}{12} \div 1\frac{5}{9}$ **15** $1\frac{11}{12} \div 9\frac{1}{5}$

16 $9\frac{3}{7} \div \frac{11}{14}$ **17** $4\frac{1}{5} \div 1\frac{1}{3}$ **18** $4\frac{7}{8} \div 2\frac{3}{5}$

19 $13\frac{1}{3} \div 1\frac{1}{9}$ **20** $3\frac{1}{5} \div 1\frac{5}{7}$ **21** $8\frac{1}{8} \div 1\frac{6}{7}$

Set 2

1 $(9 \times 10\frac{1}{4}) \div 6\frac{5}{6}$ **2** $5\frac{1}{2} \div (2\frac{1}{5} \text{ of } 1\frac{3}{10})$

3 $(15 \text{ of } \frac{3}{16}) \div 3\frac{3}{4}$ **4** $6\frac{1}{4} \times (3\frac{1}{7} \div 2\frac{4}{9})$

5 $(8\frac{2}{7} \div 9\frac{2}{3}) \text{ of } \frac{1}{2}$ **6** $(\frac{7}{18} \text{ of } 4\frac{1}{2}) \div 11\frac{2}{3}$

7 $\frac{8}{15} \div (7\frac{1}{3} \text{ of } 3\frac{1}{5})$ **8** $(1\frac{6}{17} \div 4\frac{2}{11}) \times 4\frac{1}{4}$

9 $(1\frac{4}{21} \times 2\frac{9}{10}) \div 7\frac{1}{4}$ **10** $4\frac{1}{8} \times 2\frac{1}{6} \times 3\frac{7}{11}$

11 $(3\frac{1}{8} \times 2\frac{3}{5}) \div 1\frac{1}{12}$ **12** $(\frac{2}{3} \times \frac{4}{5}) \div \frac{1}{2}$

13 $\frac{4}{9} \times 1\frac{1}{4} \times 10\frac{1}{8}$ **14** $(7\frac{3}{11} \div \frac{4}{13}) \div 1\frac{3}{10}$

FRACTIONS PROBLEMS

First try these

1 What is the value of $\frac{1}{12}$ of 192?

2 A length of timber, $1\frac{1}{4}$ m long, is cut shorter and is now $\frac{9}{10}$ of its old length. How long is it now?

3 Find the product of $6\frac{7}{8}$ and $2\frac{2}{11}$.

4 How many 600 ml bottles of milk can be filled from 15 litres of milk?

5 What is the value of $\frac{2}{5}$ of $3\frac{3}{4}$?

6 A lamp burnt $2\frac{1}{4}$ litres of paraffin every day (24 h). How many days would $7\frac{1}{2}$ litres of paraffin last? (Work as a fraction.)

7 What is the price of $4\frac{1}{2}$ m of ribbon at 14p per m?

8 How many times will $2\frac{1}{6}$ divide into $5\frac{5}{12}$?

9 (a) Multiply the greatest of the following fractions by the smallest: $1\frac{1}{4}$, $1\frac{1}{3}$, $1\frac{1}{8}$, $1\frac{1}{5}$. (b) Divide the second largest by the smallest.

10 A girl spent $\frac{1}{2}$ her money in one shop and $\frac{1}{2}$ of what remained in another. She then had 20p left. How much money had she at first?

11 Subtract $3\frac{1}{5}$ from $4\frac{2}{3}$, and divide the result by $2\frac{1}{5}$.

12 When fully loaded a lorry carries $3\frac{1}{2}$ thousand kg of sand. How much sand would it deliver in carrying $6\frac{1}{2}$ loads?

13 Tom has to walk $1\frac{3}{4}$ km to school, but Mary has to walk only $\frac{3}{7}$ as far. How far has Mary to go?

14 In an examination full marks were 100. Susan gained $\frac{9}{10}$ of full marks, and William had $\frac{2}{3}$ as many marks as Susan. How many marks did each get?

15 How many times is $\frac{7}{8}$ contained in $3\frac{1}{16}$?

16 A can holding $3\frac{7}{8}$ litres is filled 4 times with water, and each time the water is emptied into a tank. How much water is then in the tank?

17 I am $\frac{1}{4}$ the age of my father and he is $\frac{4}{7}$ as old as his father. What fraction of my grandfather's age am I?

18 Express $\frac{13}{52}$ in its lowest terms. How many times is $\frac{13}{52}$ contained in $1\frac{3}{4}$?

FRACTIONS PROBLEMS

Now try these

1 Multiply $2\frac{2}{5}$ by $\frac{5}{6}$.

2 A man travelled $\frac{5}{16}$ of a journey by rail and $\frac{4}{5}$ as far by car. The remainder of the journey was made by steamer. What fraction of the whole journey was made by car?

3 Find $4\frac{1}{2}$ times the product of $8\frac{4}{5}$ and $2\frac{3}{11}$.

4 In a car a man covers $1\frac{1}{2}$ km in 1 min. On a cycle he can travel only $\frac{1}{5}$ as fast. At what speed does he cycle? (Answer in km/h.)

5 An estate was worth £18 000·00. A man owned $\frac{5}{8}$ of it, and he sold $\frac{2}{5}$ of his share. What was the value of the part which he still had?

6 Divide $3\frac{8}{9}$ by $2\frac{1}{3}$, and add to the result $\frac{2}{7}$ of $8\frac{3}{4}$.

7 John has £36·00. Tom has $\frac{7}{18}$ as much as John, and Henry has $\frac{3}{14}$ as much as Tom. How much money has Henry?

8 Multiply $\frac{1}{4}$ by $\frac{1}{4}$, and divide the result by $\frac{1}{32}$.

9 On Monday a shopkeeper opened a 48 kg chest of tea, and he sold $\frac{5}{16}$ of the chest on that day. On Tuesday he sold $\frac{4}{5}$ as much as he did on Monday. What fraction of the whole chest did he sell on Tuesday, and what was the weight in kg?

10 How many times can $\frac{1}{2} \div \frac{3}{10}$ be taken from 5?

11 A train carried 273 passengers. Of these $\frac{3}{13}$ travelled first class. In another train there were $\frac{1}{3}$ as many passengers, and $\frac{2}{7}$ of these travelled first class. How many more first class passengers were there in the first train than in the second?

12 A bookseller sold $\frac{5}{12}$ of a gross of books at 50p each, and $\frac{4}{7}$ of the remainder at 40p. What fraction of the books had he sold, and how much money had he taken?

13 What will be the cost of $9\frac{1}{8}$ m of wire at 40p per m?

14 Janet weighs 60 kg and is $1\frac{1}{4}$ times as heavy as Mary. Kathleen weighs $\frac{11}{12}$ as much as Mary. How much does Kathleen weigh?

GENERAL REVISION

First try these

Add

1   9745
     3821
 +8695

2   £
   7·40½
  19·28
 +0·17

3 $\frac{7}{10} + \frac{3}{5} + \frac{1}{4}$

Subtract

4	weeks	days
	47	3
	−9	6

5	km	m
	5	32
	−1	87

6	litres	ml
	34	290
	−18	560

Multiply

7	kg	g
	6	158
		×2

8	h	min
	12	20
		×2

9 $8\frac{3}{4} \times 7\frac{1}{5} \times \frac{3}{16}$

Divide

10 104 litres ÷ 8   **11** 27)$\overline{869}$ **12** $8\frac{2}{9} \div 6\frac{1}{6}$

13 Write in figures twenty-eight thousand and seventy-eight.

14 If you remove 7500 ml from a 40 litre water tank, how many litres are left?

15 If I have £2·45, to how many children can I give 35p?

16 How many times can $12\frac{1}{2}$ m be cut from 175 m of ribbon?

17 Queen Victoria died in 1901 at the age of 82. In which year was she born?

18 School starts at 09:00, but I was 15 min late. Fortunately the school clock was 8 min slow. What time was it by the school clock when I arrived?

19 What is the total weight of a dozen bales, each weighing 95 kg?

20 A jet-propelled aeroplane flies at 960 km/h. A piston-engined aircraft travels at $\frac{2}{3}$ this speed, a railway engine at $\frac{1}{8}$, a racing-car at $\frac{5}{16}$ and a steamer at $\frac{1}{24}$. Find the speed at which each of these travel.

GENERAL REVISION

Now try these

Add

1 $4\frac{1}{3} + 2\frac{5}{6} + 7\frac{11}{12}$ 2 $4\frac{3}{8} + 2\frac{11}{12}$

3
kg	g
14	60
12	220
+16	540

Subtract

4
days	h
97	3
− 59	14

5 $19\frac{7}{9} - 5\frac{5}{12}$

6
litres	ml
80	75
− 36	420

Multiply

7 $\frac{2}{11} \times 4\frac{1}{8} \times \frac{7}{12}$

8
km	m
15	600
× 2	

9
398
× 47

Divide

10 $7\frac{3}{11} \div 2\frac{2}{9}$ 11 $2\frac{5}{8} \times (19\frac{1}{5} \div 84)$

12
km	m
2) 81	270

13 Write in figures sixty thousand and fifty-nine.

14 A train travels 495 km in $5\frac{1}{2}$ h. Find the speed of the train (*a*) in km/h, and (*b*) in m per sec.

15 Find the cost of the following: $\frac{3}{4}$ kg tea at 80p per kg; $1\frac{1}{2}$ kg butter at 60p per kg; 3 dozen eggs at 40p per doz.

16 Four parcels together weigh 62 kg. One of them weighs $4\frac{1}{2}$ kg more than each of the others. What is the weight of the heaviest parcel?

17 A monitor uses 1 litre of ink in filling 24 ink-wells. If 16 ml are wasted how much ink does each hold?

18 The road in which David lives is $\frac{3}{8}$ km long. The next road is $\frac{2}{5}$ of that length. How long is this road? (Answer in m.)

19 A housewife buys $1\frac{1}{2}$ litres of milk per day, at 5p per $\frac{1}{2}$ litre. What is her milk bill for the month of January?

20 Bring 726 min to h and min.

BILLS

First try these

Find the total cost of

1 1 doz. at 1p each
2 kg at 14p per kg

2 6 cm at $1\frac{1}{2}$p per cm
3 m at 7p per m

3 45 g at 12p per 30 g
$\frac{1}{2}$ litre at 22p per litre

4 8 at 3p each
5 m at 5p per m

5 36 eggs at 40p per doz.
$\frac{3}{4}$ kg at 28p per kg

6 200 kg at £12·00 per tonne
2 kg at £0·10 per kg

7 250 g at £0·16 per kg
16 litres at £0·04 per litre
5 ml at 5p per ml

8 6 doz. at 12p per doz.
1 m at $1\frac{1}{2}$p per cm
13 at 7p each

9 12 at 4 for 8p
180 g at 4p per 30 g
2 kg at $\frac{1}{2}$ kg for 10p

10 25 cm at 36p per m
$2\frac{1}{2}$ litres at 3p per litre
2 doz. at 4p each

11 18 at $1\frac{1}{2}$p each
$2\frac{1}{2}$ kg at 24p per kg
18 doz. at $\frac{1}{2}$p each

12 1 litre at 10 p per 100 ml
$2\frac{1}{2}$ doz at 15 for 75p
$\frac{1}{4}$ kg at 12p per 500 g

13 $4\frac{1}{2}$ m at £0·15 per 50 cm
20 cm at £0·60 per m
$3\frac{1}{4}$ m at £0·02 per cm

14 $1\frac{1}{2}$ litres at £0·24 per litre
50 g at £0·32 per g
4 at 20 for £0·50

15 $3\frac{3}{4}$ doz. at £0·08 per doz.
90 at £0·12 per score
12 at £0·72 per 12 doz.

16 15 m at £0·18 per cm
$1\frac{1}{2}$ litres at £0·12 per $\frac{1}{4}$ litre
$4\frac{1}{2}$ kg at £0·08 per kg

BILLS

Now try these

Find the total cost of

1 3 doz. at 6½p per doz.
4 kg at 8p per kg
2 litres at 10p per ¼ litre
9 at 7p each

2 500 g at 24p per ½ kg
17 cm at 18p per cm
25 at £2·00 per 100
10 bags at 20p per bag

3 3500 kg at £8·00 per tonne
6 kg at £1·00 per ¼ kg
3½ kg at £0·10 per kg
2 kg at £0·01 per g

4 1¼ m at 16p per cm
2½ m at 1p per cm
6¼ m at 3 m for 6p
2 m at 5½p per cm

5 ¼ kg at £5·00 per kg
250 g at £0·48 per kg
3 litres at £0·04 per ½ litre
100 at 1½p each

6 1¾ m at 36p per m
6 doz. at 2½p each
1 litre at 10p per 10 ml
750 kg at £8·00 per tonne

7 25 at £0·80 each
243 at 2p each
5 at £0·60 per doz.
6 kg at 250 g for £0·20

8 3 m at £0·31½ per m
2¼ doz. at 9 for £0·30
960 at ½p each
2¾ kg at 24p per kg

9 12 doz. eggs at £0·40 per doz.
3½ kg of butter at £0·60 per kg
4 kg of tea at £0·40 per ½ kg
2¾ kg of coffee at £0·64 ½ kg

10 6 books at £0·74 each
2 doz. comics at 6p each
7 magazines at 15p each
3 doz. at 2½p each

11 72 at ½p each
400 at 25p per 50
481 at 2p each
20 litres at 12p per litre

12 7 kg at £2·00 per ½ kg
8⅓ doz. at £5·00 per score
31 at 6p each
96 at 1½p each

PRACTICAL GEOMETRY

First try these

1 Draw straight lines which have the following lengths given in cm

   4, 5, 6, 7, 8, 9, 10, 2, 1, $1\frac{1}{2}$, $2\frac{1}{2}$
   $4\frac{1}{2}$, $6\frac{1}{2}$, $7\frac{1}{2}$, $10\frac{1}{2}$, $3\frac{1}{2}$

2 Draw squares which have sides of the following lengths given in cm, and, in each case, find the perimeter of the square.

   (a) 2   (b) 4   (c) 6   (d) 7   (e) $3\frac{1}{2}$
   (f) 5   (g) $1\frac{1}{2}$ (h) $4\frac{1}{2}$ (i) $6\frac{1}{2}$ (j) 3

3 Draw rectangles which have sides of the following lengths given in cm and, in each case, find the perimeter of the rectangle.

   (a) 2 by 3   (b) 4 by $2\frac{1}{2}$ (c) 5 by $3\frac{1}{2}$
   (d) 10 by 7   (e) 8 by 5   (f) 9 by 6
   (g) $7\frac{1}{2}$ by $4\frac{1}{2}$ (h) 2 by $6\frac{1}{2}$ (i) $3\frac{1}{2}$ by 3

4 Draw triangles which have sides of the following lengths given in cm and, in each case, find the perimeter of the triangle.

   (a) 7, 5, 4   (b) 6, 8, 10
   (c) $4\frac{1}{2}$, 6, 9   (d) $5\frac{1}{2}$, 7, $9\frac{1}{2}$
   (e) 3, $7\frac{1}{2}$, 8   (f) 10, $4\frac{1}{2}$, $8\frac{1}{2}$

5 Draw circles which have radii of the following lengths given in cm and, in each case, mark in a diameter and a radius.

   (a) 4   (b) 6   (c) 5   (d) $4\frac{1}{2}$ (e) 3
   (f) $5\frac{1}{2}$ (g) $2\frac{1}{2}$ (h) 8   (i) $6\frac{1}{2}$ (j) 7

6 Draw two circles one having a radius of 5 cm, the other having a radius of 3 cm, and their centres 8 cm apart.

PRACTICAL GEOMETRY

Now try these

1 Draw straight lines of the following lengths given in cm

$3\frac{1}{2}$, $4\frac{1}{2}$, $5\frac{1}{10}$, $6\frac{9}{10}$, $1\frac{3}{10}$, $2\frac{1}{5}$, $7\frac{4}{5}$, $8\frac{7}{10}$, $9\frac{3}{5}$, $4\frac{2}{5}$

2 Draw squares or rectangles which have sides of the following lengths given in cm, and in each case, find the perimeter

(a) $2\frac{1}{5}$ by 6   (b) $3\frac{7}{10}$ by 8   (c) 2 by $4\frac{3}{5}$

(d) 8 by 8   (e) $6\frac{9}{10}$ by $6\frac{9}{10}$ (f) 9 by $7\frac{1}{5}$

(g) $5\frac{1}{2}$ by $2\frac{1}{2}$ (h) $3\frac{1}{10}$ by $5\frac{4}{5}$ (i) $8\frac{1}{2}$ by $8\frac{1}{2}$

3 Draw triangles which have sides of the following lengths given in cm, and in each case, find the perimeter

(a) $3\frac{1}{2}$, 7, $6\frac{1}{2}$ (b) $4\frac{2}{5}$, $7\frac{3}{10}$, 5

(c) $2\frac{9}{10}$, 8, $5\frac{1}{2}$ (d) 6, $8\frac{1}{2}$, 10

4 Draw circles with radii of the following lengths given in cm

(a) $3\frac{1}{2}$ (b) 8   (c) $4\frac{3}{5}$ (d) $5\frac{3}{10}$ (e) 9

5 Copy the following figures, drawing each line the same length as it is given in the figure.

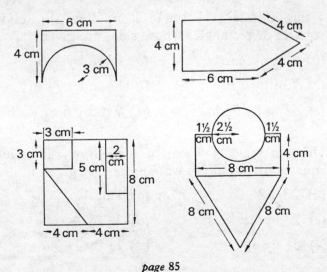

DRAWING TO SCALE

First try these

In each example, show clearly the scale of your drawing

1 Using a scale of 1 cm to 2 cm draw straight lines to represent the following distances given in cm
6, 8, 5, 9, 11, 7, 4, 10

2 Using a scale of 1 cm to 1 m draw straight lines to represent the following distances given in m
4, $2\frac{1}{2}$, 10, $6\frac{1}{2}$, 8, 9, $5\frac{1}{2}$, $7\frac{1}{2}$

3 Using a scale of 1 cm to 10 m draw straight lines to represent the following distances given in m
30, 45, 80, 75, 65, 100, 15, 55

4 Using a scale of 1 cm to 1 km draw straight lines to represent the following distances given in km
3, 5, 8, 10, $2\frac{1}{2}$, $6\frac{1}{2}$, $4\frac{1}{2}$, 9

5 Using a scale of 1 cm to 1 m, draw the following squares or rectangles whose sides are given

(a) 4 m by 2 m　　　　(b) $2\frac{1}{2}$ m by $2\frac{1}{2}$ m

(c) 7 m by 7 m　　　　(d) $8\frac{1}{2}$ m by $7\frac{1}{2}$ m

(e) $5\frac{1}{2}$ m by $5\frac{1}{2}$ m　　　(f) 9 m by 6 m

6 Using a scale of 1 cm to $\frac{1}{2}$ m draw the following squares or rectangles whose sides are given in m

(a) 2 by 2　　　　(b) 1 by $1\frac{1}{2}$

(c) $2\frac{1}{2}$ by $2\frac{1}{2}$　　　(d) $3\frac{1}{2}$ by 4

(e) $3\frac{1}{4}$ by $1\frac{3}{4}$　　　(f) $1\frac{1}{4}$ by $1\frac{1}{4}$

DRAWING TO SCALE

Now try these

In each example, show clearly the scale of the drawing

1 Using a scale of 1 cm to 1 km draw straight lines to represent the following distances given in km
   4, 7, 10, 8, 3, $2\frac{1}{2}$, $6\frac{1}{2}$, $1\frac{1}{2}$,
   $2\frac{9}{10}$, $4\frac{1}{5}$, $9\frac{3}{5}$, $6\frac{1}{10}$, $1\frac{7}{10}$, $8\frac{3}{10}$, $7\frac{2}{5}$, $3\frac{3}{5}$

2 Using a scale of 1 cm to 10 km draw straight lines to represent the following distances given in km
   20, 55, 40, 65, 28, 17, 54, 73

3 Using a scale of 1 cm to 10 m draw the following squares or rectangles whose sides are given in m

   (a) 29×19 (b) 24×30 (c) 38×40
   (d) 27×27 (e) 58×46 (f) 60×60
   (g) 73×69 (h) 84×84 (i) 90×21

4 Measure the length and breadth of the following objects. Choose a suitable scale and make a plan of each object.

   (a) A book
   (b) The top of your desk
   (c) The top of your teacher's table
   (d) A cupboard door in the classroom
   (e) The classroom door
   (f) A window
   (g) The classroom floor
   (h) The floor of the cloakroom
   (i) The floor of a corridor, or part of a corridor
   (j) The dining hall floor
   (k) The floor of the school hall
   (l) The playground, or part of the playground
   (m) The school garden, or a part of it
   (n) The playing field, or a part of it
   (o) The football or other pitch

AREA (1)

First try these

1 Find the area of each of the following squares or rectangles

	Length	Breadth		Length	Breadth
(a)	6 cm	2 cm	(b)	8 cm	5 cm
(c)	7 cm	3 cm	(d)	10 cm	$8\frac{1}{2}$ cm
(e)	4 cm	4 cm	(f)	$11\frac{1}{2}$ cm	9 cm
(g)	6 cm	6 cm	(h)	13 cm	13 cm

2 How many square cm are there in each of the following squares or rectangles?

	Length	Breadth		Length	Breadth
(a)	4 cm	3 cm	(b)	9 cm	5 cm
(c)	$3\frac{1}{2}$ cm	6 cm	(d)	8 cm	$2\frac{1}{4}$ cm
(e)	12 cm	7 cm	(f)	15 cm	15 cm
(g)	14 cm	14 cm	(h)	16 cm	$10\frac{3}{4}$ cm

3 Find the area of each of the following squares or rectangles

	Length	Breadth		Length	Breadth
(a)	5 m	6 m	(b)	7 m	7 m
(c)	$10\frac{1}{2}$ m	8 m	(d)	15 m	11 m
(e)	14 m	$8\frac{1}{2}$ m	(f)	20 m	$5\frac{1}{4}$ m
(g)	17 m	17 m	(h)	24 m	$3\frac{3}{4}$ m

4 How many square cm are there in

(a) 2 sq m   (b) 3 sq m   (c) $\frac{1}{2}$ sq m

(d) $3\frac{1}{2}$ sq m   (e) $1\frac{1}{2}$ sq m   (f) $2\frac{1}{2}$ sq m

(g) $1\frac{1}{4}$ sq m   (h) $4\frac{1}{4}$ sq m   (i) $4\frac{3}{4}$ sq m

AREA (1)

Now try these

1 Find the area of each of the following squares or rectangles

	Length	Breadth		Length	Breadth
(a)	$3\frac{1}{5}$ cm	$2\frac{1}{2}$ cm	(b)	$5\frac{1}{4}$ cm	$3\frac{1}{5}$ cm
(c)	$4\frac{1}{2}$ cm	$2\frac{2}{5}$ cm	(d)	$11\frac{1}{4}$ cm	$8\frac{4}{5}$ cm
(e)	12 cm	$10\frac{3}{4}$ cm	(f)	16 cm	$9\frac{1}{2}$ cm
(g)	$17\frac{1}{2}$ cm	$3\frac{1}{2}$ cm	(h)	$6\frac{3}{4}$ cm	$9\frac{1}{3}$ cm

2 How many square m are there in each of the following carpets?

	Length	Breadth		Length	Breadth
(a)	$9\frac{1}{2}$ m	8 m	(b)	12 m	13 m
(c)	$12\frac{1}{2}$ m	18 m	(d)	$6\frac{1}{2}$ m	$10\frac{1}{2}$ m
(e)	16 m	17 m	(f)	$11\frac{1}{5}$ m	15 m
(g)	$12\frac{3}{4}$ m	$12\frac{3}{4}$ m	(h)	$10\frac{1}{4}$ m	20 m

3 Find the area of each of the following gardens

	Length	Breadth		Length	Breadth
(a)	9 m	9 m	(b)	11 m	12 m
(c)	14 m	18 m	(d)	16 m	15 m
(e)	21 m	21 m	(f)	13 m	13 m
(g)	$22\frac{1}{2}$ m	17 m	(h)	27 m	21 m

4 Find how many square cm there are in
(a) $1\frac{7}{8}$ sq m   (b) $2\frac{1}{2}$ sq m   (c) $3\frac{3}{4}$ sq m

5 Find how many square m there are in
(a) 20 000 sq cm   (b) 35 000 sq cm   50 000 sq cm

AREA (2)

First try these

1 Find the breadth of each of the following rectangles, given the area of the figure and its length

	Area	Length		Area	Length
(a)	50 sq cm	5 cm	(b)	27 sq cm	3 cm
(c)	84 sq cm	12 cm	(d)	77 sq cm	7 cm
(e)	72 sq cm	9 cm	(f)	56 sq cm	8 cm
(g)	44 sq cm	11 cm	(h)	48 sq cm	4 cm

2 Find the length of each of the following rectangles, given the area of the figure and its breadth

	Area	Breadth		Area	Breadth
(a)	120 sq cm	12 cm	(b)	80 sq cm	16 cm
(c)	28 sq cm	4 cm	(d)	68 sq cm	17 cm
(e)	54 sq m	6 m	(f)	63 sq m	9 m
(g)	98 sq m	7 m	(h)	132 sq m	11 m

3 Find the length of the side of the square having the area given

(a)	9 sq cm	(b) 36 sq m	(c)	81 sq cm
(d)	100 sq m	(e) 25 sq m	(f)	121 sq cm
(g)	16 sq m	(h) 49 sq cm	(i)	25 sq m
(j)	144 sq cm	(k) 64 sq m	(l)	169 sq cm

4 How many square m are there in
(a) 30 000 sq cm (b) 45 000 sq cm (c) 75 000 sq cm
(d) 22 500 sq cm (e) 37 500 sq cm (f) 100 000 sq cm

AREA (2)

Now try these

1 Find the length of each of the following rectangles, given the area of the figure and its breadth

	Area	Breadth		Area	Breadth
(a)	55 sq cm	10 cm	(b)	$67\frac{1}{2}$ sq m	9 m
(c)	39 sq cm	6 cm	(d)	58 sq km	8 km
(e)	$45\frac{1}{2}$ sq m	7 m	(f)	100 sq m	12 m
(g)	108 sq cm	9 cm	(h)	18 sq km	4 km
(i)	225 sq m	12 m	(j)	169 sq m	13 m
(k)	$32\frac{1}{2}$ sq km	5 km	(l)	$60\frac{1}{2}$ sq cm	11 cm

2 Find the breadth of each of the following rectangles given the area of the figure and its length

	Area	Length		Area	Length
(a)	110 sq cm	11 cm	(b)	54 sq cm	12 cm
(c)	256 sq m	16 m	(d)	$130\frac{1}{2}$ sq cm	9 cm
(e)	$61\frac{1}{4}$ sq km	7 km	(f)	$97\frac{1}{2}$ sq cm	5 cm
(g)	84 sq m	$10\frac{1}{2}$ m	(h)	$16\frac{1}{4}$ sq m	$3\frac{1}{4}$ m
(i)	19 sq km	$4\frac{3}{4}$ km	(j)	81 sq m	6 m
(k)	273 sq cm	13 cm	(l)	$94\frac{1}{2}$ sq m	9 m

3 Find the length of the side of the square having the area given

(a) 225 sq km   (b) 196 sq km   (c) 289 sq km

(d) $6\frac{1}{4}$ sq cm   (e) $2\frac{1}{4}$ sq m   (f) $20\frac{1}{4}$ sq m

4 How many square m are there in
(a) 200 000 sq cm (b) 375 000 sq cm (c) 530 000 sq cm

AREA (3)

First try these

1 Find the area of the following figures. Note very carefully the lengths of the sides.

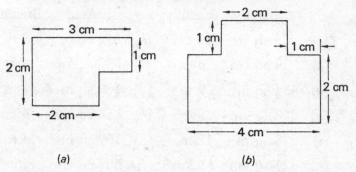

(a)   (b)

2 Find the area of the shaded portions of the following figures

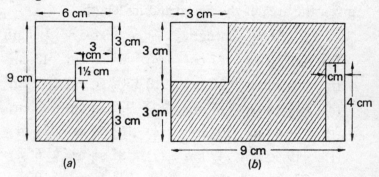

(a)   (b)

3 From a carpet, 3 m long and 2 m wide, a rectangle measuring $1\frac{1}{2}$ m by 1 m was cut out. What area of carpet remained?

4 On a table $1\frac{1}{2}$ m long and 1 m wide is a cloth which has an area of $1\frac{1}{4}$ sq m. What area of table remains uncovered?

5 How many rectangular pieces of metal, each 5 cm long and 3 cm wide, can be cut from a rectangular sheet of metal 30 cm long and 18 cm wide?

AREA (3)

Now try these

1 Find the area of the following figures. Note very carefully the lengths of the sides.

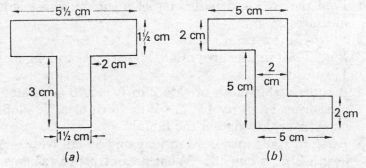

(a)   (b)

2 Find the area of the shaded portions of the following figures

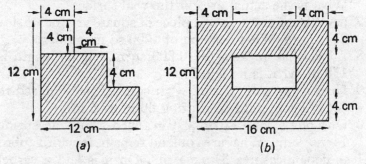

(a)   (b)

3 On a white square, measuring 6 m by 6 m, a square, measuring $5\frac{1}{2}$ m by $5\frac{1}{2}$ m, was painted red. What area of the larger square remained white?

4 A concrete path 1 m wide was laid round a rectangular lawn measuring 5 m by 4 m. What was the area of concrete laid?

5 A rectangular sheet of metal 10 cm by 6 cm has four square holes cut in it, each of which has a side 2 cm long. How many square cm of metal are left in the sheet?

AREA PROBLEMS

First try these

Make a rough drawing wherever possible, and put in the measurements.

1 Find the area and perimeter of a square whose side measures $3\frac{1}{4}$ cm.

2 What is the area of a carpet 5 m by $4\frac{1}{2}$ m?

3 Find, in sq m, the area of a table-cloth $1\frac{1}{2}$ m long and $1\frac{1}{4}$ m wide.

4 A square table-cloth of side 2 m is placed on a table measuring $1\frac{3}{4}$ m by $1\frac{1}{4}$ m. What area of table-cloth hangs over the edge of the table?

5 A roll of wallpaper is 12 m long and 54 cm wide. A length 2 m is cut off. What area of paper remains?

6 One side of the wall of a room is 6 m long and $2\frac{1}{4}$ m high. A door in the wall is 2 m high and 1 m wide. What is the actual area of the wall surface?

7 (a) What is the area of a piece of square ground of side 25 m? (b) What fraction of 1000 sq m is this?

8 A field has an area of 10 500 sq m. If its length is 150 m, what is its width?

9 How many stones, each $\frac{1}{4}$ m square, are required to cover a courtyard measuring 80 m by 5 m?

10 On a plot of land 120 m × 70 m a shed is built measuring 14 m × 9 m. What area of land remains for cultivation?

11 A floor measures 5 m × 4 m. On it is laid a carpet $3\frac{1}{4}$ m × $3\frac{1}{4}$ m. What area of floor is left uncovered?

12 What is the area, in sq m, of 24 panes of glass each 1 m × $\frac{3}{4}$ m?

13 A rectangular field has an area of 5 hectares. If it has a width of 100 m, what is its length? (1 hectare = 10 000 sq m.)

14 A football pitch is 110 m long and 74 m wide. (a) What is its area in sq m? (b) How much short of 1 hectare is this?

AREA PROBLEMS

Now try these

Make a rough drawing wherever possible, and put in the measurements.

1 A roll of carpet was 36 m long and 70 cm wide. After three lengths, 5 m, 7 m and 10 m, have been cut off, how many square m of carpet remained?

2 A red square of side 1 m is surrounded by a blue border $\frac{2}{5}$ m wide. What is the area of the border?

3 Find the cost of $5\frac{1}{2}$ m of material, 120 cm wide, at £1·20 per sq m.

4 The area of a passage is $10\frac{1}{2}$ sq m, and the width is 100 cm. How long is the passage?

5 A piece of ground is 130 sq m in area. How much ground must be added to it in order to make its area equal to that of a square of side 13 m?

6 Pieces of cardboard are 20 cm × 30 cm. How many must be placed together to cover an area 4 m × 6 m?

7 A roll contains 1000 sq m of paper. If the paper is $1\frac{1}{4}$ m wide, how many m long is the roll?

8 A table-cloth, 100 cm × 100 cm, has a border 10 cm wide sewn on to it. What is the area of the border? (Answer in sq cm.)

9 A field measuring 180 m by 75 m has wooden palings, which are 1 m apart, all round it. Find (a) the area of the field, (b) its perimeter, (c) the number of palings required.

10 A hearth measures 2 m × $\frac{3}{5}$ m. If it is made of tiles 40 cm × 20 cm, how many tiles are there?

11 The area of a rectangle is 57 sq cm, and its length is $9\frac{1}{2}$ cm. What is its perimeter?

12 A sheet of metal measures 4 m × $1\frac{1}{2}$ m. How many squares of side 10 cm can be cut from it?

13 What is the cost of covering a rectangular-shaped room with linoleum, at £1·25 per sq m, if the room measures 6 m × 4 m?

14 After laying a carpet 5 m × 5 m, a margin of $\frac{1}{2}$ m all round is left bare. Find the area of the floor.

GENERAL REVISION

All can try these

Add

1

km	m
13	250
7	64
+42	983

2 $\frac{4}{9} + \frac{3}{4} + 1\frac{5}{6}$

3

kg	g
17	84
24	136
+21	715

Subtract

4

litres	ml
10	410
- 7	625

5

min	sec
50	2
-40	39

6

30 207
- 19 413

Multiply

7 13 cm × 9 cm

8 $2\frac{1}{12} \times 4\frac{1}{5} \times \frac{1}{10}$

9

472
× 39

Divide

10 132 sq m ÷ 12 m

11 $9\frac{5}{7} \div 1\frac{3}{14}$

12 $£$
$11\overline{)126 \cdot 50}$

13 Write in figures ninety-nine thousand and ninety-nine.

14 On a map 1 cm stands for 1 km. I walk 5 km along a road away from home and $1\frac{1}{2}$ km back. How far am I now from home, and what distance on the map represents this?

15 How many 75 g packets can be made from $4\frac{3}{4}$ kg of sweets, and how much is left over?

16 The side of a square field is 120 m long. A fence is put round the field, leaving space for two gates, each 4 m wide. Find the length of fencing used.

17 By how much is 10 000 greater than five times 929?

18 A rectangular plot of ground is 50 m × 35 m. What is its area?

19 A train left London at 19:20 and arrived at Inverness (in the north of Scotland) at 08:00 the next day. How many minutes was it on the journey?